Robert Hume

Equiano
The slave with the
loud voice

and his fight against the slave trade

Illustrated by Cheryl Ives

Stone
Publishing
House

First published in 2007
Stone Publishing House
17 Stone House
North Foreland Road
Broadstairs
Kent CT10 3NT

ISBN: 978-0-9549909-1-6

Typeset in 13pt Bembo by Troubador Publishing Ltd, Leicester, UK
Printed in Great Britain by
The Cromwell Press Ltd, Trowbridge, Wilts

Robert Hume is Head of History at Clarendon House Grammar School, Ramsgate. He has written several non-fiction books, a historical novel and two children's books *The Boy who would be King: Perkin Warbeck* and *Dr Joseph Bell: the original Sherlock Holmes*.

Equiano

The slave with the loud voice

Chapter 1

'Eat it, curse you!'

The ship was not yet half way across the Atlantic on the journey from West Africa, and the mate's patience was already running thin. He knew that his cargo of black slaves had to arrive in the West Indies safe and sound. Dead slaves would mean lost profits. So there was certainly no place for hunger strikers.

The slave closed his eyes and lowered his head. The bowl he was holding crashed to the deck, spilling its contents of horse beans. The slaves hated horse beans. But the slave captains loved them, as they were nutritious and, above all, cheap.

'Take him below!' the mate shouted through his beard. His breath reeked of rum.

'Yes, sir!' replied two sailors.

One sailor, with mean lips and a ponytail, kicked away a piece of sail cloth that the slave had been mending, while the other unlocked the chains tying the slave to the side of the ship. They dragged him to his feet and shoved him towards the stern. His chains clanked along the deck, his leg irons tore into his knees, almost to the bone. When the ship rolled, he stumbled. But the sailors soon forced him to his feet again.

At length, he reached the ship's hole. The slaves called it the 'hell hole' because the air was putrid and rank with excrement and vomit – crews said you could smell it a mile away at sea.

The sailors gripped the slave's wrists and made him climb down the rope ladder with his manacled hands. Below, in the dark, lay the shadowy figures of the diseased and dying – rows and rows of them (for the captain was a 'tight packer'), all chained together – men and women alike – some chanting a song about Africa, others wailing in pain.

'Where shall we put him?' asked the one with the ponytail.

'Right there!' yelled the mate.

The sailors threw him to the deck and ponytail pinned the slave's shoulders against the ship's side with his knees. The other sailor fastened the irons around his ankles. Meanwhile, the mate went off to fetch something. He returned a few moments later with what looked like a very large pair of dividers, the kind that a dentist might use to keep your jaws wide open. Those in the know called the device a *speculum oris*. The sailors didn't have a word for it.

The mate began to fumble with a screw on the side of the instrument. But nothing happened.

'Damnation and curses!'

He passed the *speculum* to one of the sailors, but he could not get it to turn either. So he tried bashing it against the deck. Eventually, the screw turned and the instrument began to open.

'Open your mouth, curse you!'

Using his thumb and forefinger, the mate

managed to part the slave's lips a fraction of an inch. Then he tried to prize apart his upper and lower teeth.

'Right, push it in… now!'

The sailor tried inserting the *speculum* into the slave's mouth.

'Beans ready… curses!'

The mate withdrew a bleeding finger.

'I'll get you to eat these beans, damn you! Fetch me a coal from the furnace!'

A boy of about ten scurried off.

He returned shortly, cradling a piece of glinting coal in a rag. But it was so hot that he had to let it drop.

The boy looked at it helplessly.

'Sorry sir!' he whimpered.

The mate grabbed a thick piece of cloth from the deck and seized the coal.

There was a steely glint in his eyes. They were the eyes of a madman.

'You'll open your mouth all right now! Be ready with those beans!'

The mate pressed the burning cinder tightly

against his captive's lips. The slave let out a fearful howl. Then, while the mate held his head back, the sailor inserted the *speculum* again. This time it slid in easily.

'Beans!'

The sloppy mixture was poured down the slave's throat. But he refused to swallow and started to spew them out again.

'I'll get him to swallow!'

The mate punched his throat.

'You dare prefer death to slavery!'

As the slave coughed and spluttered, the mate looked around triumphantly. The rows and rows of slaves were now all deadly silent.

'And anyone else who tries this on will get the same treatment!'

★ ★ ★

During the 17th, 18th and early 19th centuries, nearly fourteen million slaves were taken in conditions similar to these from their homes on the west coast of

Africa on the dreaded 'Middle Passage' to the West Indies as part of what has become known as the 'triangular trade'. When they arrived, most were forced to work in fields called plantations – planting, weeding and harvesting tobacco, sugar and cotton – from sunrise to sunset. Each morning when they woke, many had no idea even for whom they would be working, whose whip would lash them. This was because some masters did not actually own plantations themselves, but hired their slaves out by the day.

Several European countries took part in the trade but over half the slaves were transported in British ships. Generations of merchants from Liverpool, Bristol and London depended on the slave trade to make a rich living. They described themselves not as slavers but as 'adventurers' taking part in the 'respectable trade.' Their elegant houses in the most fashionable districts of these cities were living proof of how profitable the trade was, and they were determined that it should continue to enrich their families.

However, one of its victims, a black slave from

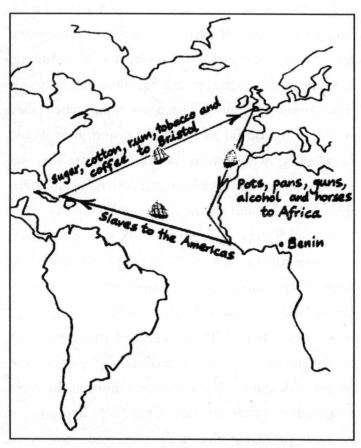

Map 1: Britain and the 'Triangular trade'

modern-day Nigeria on the west coast of Africa, managed, against all the odds, to make a courageous stand against the slave trade. His name was Equiano. This is his story.

Chapter 2

Equiano tells us, in his own words, that he was born in Africa in 1745, in a village far inland, which lay in a beautiful valley in the province of Essaka, deep in the kingdom of Benin. He had never heard of white men and had never seen the sea.

He had six older brothers and one sister. His father was a chief, whose job was to settle disputes and punish crimes. It was easy enough for him to make decisions because the law was simple – just a matter of straightforward retaliation. An eye for an eye, and a tooth for a tooth. If, let's say, a man was found guilty of kidnapping a boy, Equiano's father

Map 2: Africa's slave coast

would make him give up one of his own slaves as a punishment.

Cut into his forehead was a special mark to show how important he was – a mark that Equiano himself was destined to receive. And if asked how good a chief he was expected to become, his first name, Olaudah, provided a vital clue. It meant 'one favoured' and 'having a loud voice.' And when he was very young he was indeed shown favour when a poisonous snake had wriggled between his feet but did not bite him. As for his 'loud voice' that was to be crucial to him later in life.

In the valley, men, women and children worked in the fields, cultivating corn and peppers, bananas, yams and pineapples. The women also spun cotton and dyed it, using juice from berries, until it became a beautiful shade of bright blue. Men and women would wrap the cloth around their bodies to form a tunic. There was so much to do, nobody was idle and there were no beggars.

Slaves worked alongside free men – Equiano says that his father owned many slaves. They were not treated badly: they did no more work than other people, and their food, clothing and lodging were the same as for those who were free. Life was simple and the people were cheerful, easy to get along with. They were happy. They did not need to swear at one another or curse. In fact, the worst expressions Equiano could remember were 'may you rot!' and 'may a beast take you!'

They had festivals where they would sing and dance, play the drums, strum guitars and shake rattles. Once, when he was about four or five years old, Equiano remembered an amazing display of dancing. His people had just won an important battle and wanted to celebrate. There were four groups of dancers. The first group was made up of married men carrying broad swords and waving banners as if they were going to war. The second comprised married women, holding high in the air the earthenware and tobacco pipes they had made. A third group was formed of sporting young men carrying bows and arrows; while a fourth group of young maidens carried nothing at all, apart that is from their innocence and their radiant smiles.

The dance over, they would disperse to their homes. Equiano's father owned a large piece of ground surrounded with a fence. Within this were houses for the family and the slaves. They were easy to put up as the whole neighbourhood would help. Provided you invited them to a feast afterwards!

In the centre was his father's own house with one room for him to sit in during the day; the other to entertain his friends in. On one side were the sleeping quarters of his father and brothers. On the other side his mother and his sister slept. The sleeping rooms were covered on all sides and plastered inside with a cow-dung mix so as to keep away insects during the night. Equiano's bed consisted of a platform three or four feet off the ground and his blankets were animal skins.

When he and his brothers woke in the morning they would see their God, looking down at them from his place in the sun, smoking his pipe. It was he who controlled everything that happened to them – their fate in battle, when it was their time to die. While they were alive, their ancestors watched over them. To show respect at mealtimes, after they had washed their hands, Equiano and his family would put aside a little food and drink for their ancestors. This way they would guard them from evil spirits and enemies.

But in the forest outside the village, life was more dangerous. Among the trees, bandits and thieves could be hiding.

One day, when Equiano was eleven years old, his parents had gone to work in the fields as usual. He and his sister were left alone to look after the house. Suddenly, two men and a woman climbed over the fence. In an instant they grabbed them both. They stuffed rags into their mouths. They tied their hands. Then off they ran with them into the woods. When night came they sheltered in a small house where the robbers unbound them and they slept.

As the sun rose, they were tied up again and continued through the woods. At last they came to a road that Equiano thought he knew. In the distance he saw some people and called out to them for help. This made the robbers angry, they tied him up more tightly and bundled him into a large sack. Next day he and his sister were separated. He was so upset that he could not eat anything for days, apart from what was forced into his mouth.

Over the next few months he was to have several masters. He was with his first master, a goldsmith, for about a month, and his job was to work a pair of bellows to pump air into a furnace. In the evenings he would help the young women carry pitchers of water from the springs to the house.

All the while he tried to keep track of the direction in which his home lay. He was determined to escape at the first opportunity. But then something awful happened that upset his plans.

He used to help an elderly woman slave to cook and look after the chickens. One morning when he was feeding them he threw a pebble at one that was taking more than its fair share of corn. He had not meant to do it any harm but unfortunately the pebble killed the poor creature. Equiano quickly buried it and thought that would be the end of the matter. However, a few days later, the cook asked him where the chicken was. Equiano had been brought up by his mother always to tell the truth but when he told the old woman what had happened she flew into a terrible rage and said he would suffer for it. Her master was out so she went to tell her mistress, an absolute dragon who would think nothing of giving him a right good beating. So Equiano ran away and hid in the woods.

When the old woman returned with her mistress, Equiano was, of course, nowhere to be seen. So they searched the house from top to bottom, calling out his name. Before long, all the neighbours were helping, too, and from time to time he heard a rustling in the trees. If he were caught he would be punished. He could hear men talking, but they never quite reached him. He heard a voice say 'He'll never get out. He'll be lost forever in the woods.' These words made him frightened, and his fears turned to panic when dusk fell. Perhaps he would never make it home but would perish in the woods.

That night, feeling faint and hungry – for he had not eaten or drunk all day – he crept out of the woods and made it to his master's kitchen, where he laid down in the ashes of the fireplace and soon fell asleep.

Early the next morning the old woman slave came down to light the fire and could not believe her eyes to see Equiano there. She promptly went to fetch her master. Both of them were so pleased to see him again that he got off with a mild scolding. In view of their kindness, how could he ever think of trying to escape again?

Soon afterwards, the goldsmith's daughter suddenly died and the father became very depressed. So depressed that, if his neighbours had not watched him carefully, he might have killed himself. But when he was well again he found that he could manage perfectly without his young slave boy and decided to sell him.

Equiano describes how he was carried 'to the left of the sun's rising, through many dreary wastes and dismal woods' where wild beasts roared. His captors were not bad people and when he was tired they carried him on their shoulders or on their backs. And when, one evening, he met up with his sister they let him stay with her. It was to be their last night together; they would never see one another again.

After travelling many miles they came to the beautiful African town of Tinmah where he was sold for one hundred and seventy-two little white shells to a strangely spoken merchant with horrible looks, a red face and long hair. The man had only bought him to make money, for within three days he had sold him on to a wealthy widow for a handsome profit. She took him to her house – one of the finest Equiano had ever seen – where he was washed and perfumed, and introduced to her only son who was of about his own age. The widow and her son treated him so well that he forgot he was a slave. They even allowed him to eat and drink with them. For the next couple of months he was happy. But one night, while the widow and her son were asleep, all this suddenly came to an end when he was dragged outside by a group of men, bound and gagged, and taken away in the direction of the coast.

Eventually, Equiano reached a region where the people were different from any he had experienced before. They had completely different customs and manners. They ate without washing their hands and cooked in iron pots. For weapons they used European cutlasses and cross bows. Their skin was full of scars and their teeth were filed sharp. They offered to decorate his skin with scars and file his teeth sharp but he would not let them.

After about six months Equiano arrived on the African coast. The first thing that caught his eye was the very white sand and the sea – a vast sheet of water, glistening in the sunlight. The next thing was a ship that rested at anchor a short distance out to sea where the water was deeper. There were several decks, which made the ship float high in the water. Great pieces of cloth rippled in the breeze, and were so tall that no matter how much he craned his neck he could not see where they ended.

His captors passed him to the ship's surgeon, who tossed him up in the air to check that he was fit and healthy. After that he was ferried out to the ship in a rowing boat and carried on board. Sailors with peculiar blotchy complexions and long hair leered down at him. When they spoke they did so in a very strange language.

He gave his name to the captain, who snorted and noted him down in the ship's register as 'Jacob'. Equiano had already been deprived of his freedom and family. He had become merely an object, a possession. Now he was even having his name taken away from him.

Several days passed. On the morning they set sail on their long journey to the West Indies, a gun was fired as they sailed out into deeper water. Equiano looked down at the sea and envied the fish their freedom. If only he could change places with them.

From time to time he also saw flying fish which surprised him very much. They would fly across the ship, and many of them fell on the deck. He also saw the sailors using a strange instrument they called a quadrant. They told him that they needed it in order to work out the altitude of the sun and the latitude of any given place. One day, seeing that he was interested, one of the sailors let him peep through it. The clouds appeared to him to be land. But if it was land, it disappeared as they sailed along which could not be right. Equiano was convinced that he had entered another world and that everything he saw around him was magic.

A white sailor brought him some liquor in a glass, but he was too afraid to take it. Who knew what poison these wicked white people might be giving him? So one of the black slaves took it and gave it to him. He told him that it was safe and would make him feel better. The strongest thing Equiano had ever drunk before was palm wine. Reluctantly, he tried some. But all it did was produce a very strange feeling at the back of his throat.

The sailors brought food. He suspected that there was something wrong with it and refused that too. His refusal was like showing a red rag to a bull. In an instant the sailors grabbed hold of him, laid him across the windlass and flogged him. After that he was taken below deck where the women shrieked and the dying groaned. The heat and the stench were suffocating. All around him were black people of every description, chained together. It was so crowded that you had scarcely room to turn. And, if you could turn, you might easily find your feet in a stinking syrupy sludge of urine and sewage which swished to and fro in a big trough the sailors called the 'necessary tub.' He wanted to die. 'I now wished for the last friend, death, to relieve me,' he wrote in his autobiography many years later. That way he would return to where he was born – Africa. But the captain had already thought of that and had taken measures to prevent slaves committing suicide by tying a great sheet of netting around the ship.

He spoke to some of the other slaves.

A reply came in a soft, lilting voice, the voice of a boy not much older than himself, very thin and dirty.

'We are being taken to the white people's country.'

'Country? What country?' asked Equiano.

At first the boy did not answer.

'It is a long way off. They will find work for us there.'

He did not believe a word of it. Why should these white people help them? They never shared any decent food with them. And they looked more brutal and cruel than anyone he had ever seen before.

★ ★ ★

Equiano had not learned to trust them any better when, many weeks later, the ship weighed anchor at Bridgetown, Barbados, in the West Indies.

Before they were taken ashore, the ship's surgeon made the slaves as presentable as possible. Sores were covered up and skin was rubbed down with palm oil and made glossy. They were made to jump up and down, and weighed, so that they could be sold 'by the lump,' just like a piece of meat. Then they were taken below deck again and made to wait. He was full of doom and gloom; he wanted to die, to return to Africa, to be reunited with his family.

At last, the whites led them away. They passed men on horseback and strange houses of brick, several storeys high. Mile after mile they went until they came to a merchant's yard. Gates were flung open and they were herded inside. All around them were rolls of cloth and sacks that looked as though they might contain rice.

A day passed. A stout man with a wide-brimmed hat was beating a drum. Men were rushing into the yard, coming across to the slaves, turning them over, looking for any blemishes – just as you might do if you were buying apples in a supermarket. But this was Bridgetown and it was a slave auction. Planters watched from behind the fence, where a poster gave details of the cargo to be sold – healthy Negroes – men, boys, women and girls.

The Africans sat in chains, around posts in the

middle of the yard, their heads bent low. The auctioneer stepped on to a platform. The selling was under way. Bids were allowed in gold bars, rum, tobacco, brandy, gunpowder, whatever.

'Who will make an offer for Hannibal here? Thirty years old. He'll make a very good labourer. Do I hear 180 gallons of rum?'

The auctioneer looked around expectantly but only for a few moments. Bids started to come in fast and furiously.

'And what can I hear for Eliza? You won't find a better washerwoman anywhere!'

Then a man with a stick prodded Equiano and made him get to his feet.

'And what for Jacob here?' asked the auctioneer.

Buyers were now heading off with their purchases towards their plantations all over Barbados. There they would be branded like cattle with their master's initials. Brothers and sisters were being separated. Children were being taken from their parents.

What fate awaited Equiano?

Chapter 3

Several hours must have passed. Nobody wanted to buy Equiano or the other very young slaves. Barbados sugar planters preferred strong, full-grown males. No one who was less than four foot in height or who was too old stood a chance. The slave masters described them as 'unserviceable.' And certainly no one in their right senses would have bought these tiddlers. They knew they would not get much work out of them, and that was assuming they would settle at all (the slave masters called it 'seasoning') which seemed doubtful as they were pining too much for their families.

So they were taken from the West Indies to the North American mainland. On their arrival in Virginia they were put to work on Mr Campbell's tobacco plantation – weeding and gathering stones.

After a few weeks, there was not enough work for them all, and they were dispatched to different plantations in Virginia. Only Equiano was kept on, and he was now mostly involved with household chores.

One day, when Mr Campbell had a fever, Equiano was asked to fetch a fan. He was a grumpy man at the best of times, and worse still when he was ill. As he hurried along to his master's room he happened to pass the kitchen where a new black woman slave was cooking. The very instant he saw her he dropped the fan. He could scarcely believe his eyes – over her mouth was an iron muzzle. It looked so tight that she surely could not speak, let alone eat or drink. No slave was ever treated like this back in Africa. Leaving the fan on the floor, he dashed outside. He knew only too well that there were worse things that could happen to female slaves. He had heard the stories of young women, sometimes even children, being raped by their owners. The bastard children that were born would in turn be used as slaves. They would work in the fields, be whipped for not working hard enough and sold on when it pleased their owners. All these were worse things without a doubt. But this slave woman was actually in front of him, right now, and she was wearing a muzzle. That couldn't be right.

When he had calmed down, a servant led him to a room at the back of the house. The shutters were closed and his master was slumped in a basket chair, asleep. His mouth was wide open, showing a gold tooth. As he breathed, his big belly rose up and down. Why were the white slave owners so fat? In Africa the slave owners were no fatter than their slaves.

As Equiano fanned his master, he looked around the room. It gave him the creeps. Everything was so gloomy. On the chimney stack was a clock with an incredibly loud tick. Weird! Perhaps it could tell his master anything he did wrong, even what he was

thinking. Who knows? On the wall was a picture of an old man. The eyes seemed to stare down at him. It freaked him out! What a peculiar lot were these people from Virginia, and what strange possessions they had.

* * *

Some weeks later, the captain of a merchant ship came to the house on business and Equiano was asked to bring in some refreshments. The captain, whose name was Michael Pascal, liked the look of Equiano, and held him up to see how heavy he was. After a few moments thought he made Mr Campbell an offer of forty pounds for him.

Silence. Pascal stood there, cracking his knuckles.

'Done!' said Campbell.

Pascal was convinced he had a bargain. Besides, if Equiano didn't live up to expectation, he would make a nice little present for his cousins in London.

And so the next day Equiano was taken on horseback to the Virginian coast where he was led on board a large ship called the *Industrious Bee*, loaded with tobacco for the merchants of Bristol.

It was quite usual for masters to rename their slaves to show that they owned them, and Captain Pascal was no different to the rest. From now onwards, Equiano was to be called Gustavus Vassa. What a sick sense of humour Pascal must have had. Gustavus Vassa was the name of a former King of Sweden who had been powerful and respected – whereas Equiano, an African, had no power and was not respected. If he had to be called anything, why not Jacob – the name he had been used to? But the captain would have none of it and cuffed him round the ear when he refused to answer to his new name.

The *Industrious Bee* had a very long journey before it – some fifteen hundred miles back to England – and to make provisions last the captain began rationing them. In the last leg of the journey food was so short that they had to make do with one and a half pound of bread per week and the same amount of meat. For drink, they were restricted to just two pints of water per day.

'We'll have to kill and eat YOU!' said the captain.

They were just having a laugh but Equiano was terrified that they were serious and meant what they said. Then, to his relief, one day the crew caught a large shark and pulled it on board. Food! What a let-off! It would take the crew's minds off thinking about eating him. But to his astonishment they cut off a bit of the tail and tossed the rest back over the side. Perhaps he might still be eaten after all!

Fortunately he was able to share his worries. On board was a white American lad about five years older than Equiano. His name was Richard Baker and his family was friendly with the captain. Richard explained that Captain Pascal was always mucking around and joking, and that he had threatened to kill and eat HIM before now. But Equiano could not see the funny side.

Richard was not the slightest bit bothered that Equiano was black or that he was a slave, and soon they became good friends. Richard promised to teach him to read. Equiano had often seen Captain Pascal and Richard reading books. One in particular had caught his attention. It was about the explorer Christopher Columbus and his voyages in the West Indies. They mouthed the words as they read and it was easy for Equiano to believe that they must be talking to the books. He took up the book about Columbus and talked to it. He put an ear to it, hoping that it would answer. But it stayed silent. Why was this? Was it because his skin was black?

Chapter 4

Spring 1757. After thirteen long weeks, the *Industrious Bee* finally berthed at Falmouth in Cornwall. Equiano had been treated well on board, with sails to lie on and, until the last leg of the journey, with good food to eat. They now lay at anchor for some weeks.

One bitterly cold morning when he got up on deck it was all covered with salt. Had some joker thrown it over the deck during the night? Equiano went to gather up a handful. But as he did so he found that it was ice cold. He took it down to the mate, who asked him to taste it.

'It's snow!' he said. 'Don't you have snow in your country?'

Equiano didn't answer.

'Well?'

'No,' Equiano replied, puzzled.

'It's made by a great man in the heavens, called God.'

Equiano repeated the words slowly. 'God... God.'

The mate shook his head in disbelief. This boy must be some sort of idiot!

Equiano's innocence about snow was to be shattered a few hours later when they were caught in a severe snow shower. The wind whipped up, and sharp crystals of snow cut into his face and eyes like pin points. And how they stung!

When the weather had improved they sailed for the small island of Guernsey in the English Channel, where the ship's owner lived. Equiano and Richard were given board and lodging with a family who treated them kindly and let them play with their children. He soon developed a soft spot for their five year old daughter who had a beautiful complexion. Every morning he would watch her mother wash the girl's face until it looked very rosy. Curiously, when she washed Equiano's face nothing happened. He just couldn't make out why.

He was still scrubbing his face to try and make it white when summer arrived and he and Richard were given orders to leave Guernsey and set sail for London. There he would meet up with Captain Pascal again. War was raging between England and France over who should control Canada and its precious fur trade. Any time now his master would be recalled to war and he would be taking the boys with him. Equiano was not even twelve years old and was not a British citizen but he would still be expected to take part. Until the call to war came they would be free to explore London, and they were both very excited at the prospect.

But just as they were about to reach the mouth of the River Thames they sighted a small man-of-war. A cry came up from the helm: 'IT'S THE PRESS GANG!' The press gang only had one thing on their mind – to recruit on to their ship fit and healthy sailors who would fight against the French in Canada. They were just like those who had violently kidnapped him and his sister in Africa.

If they were captured it would be a disaster! Captain Pascal had been treating the boys well. But now there was the prospect of them being shipped off to Canada, hundreds of miles away. There was no way of knowing what their new captain might be like. And besides, there would be no exploring London!

What could they do? What would you have done?

They could jump into the water. Richard might make it ashore but Equiano did not know how to swim. They would probably never make it. They would be spotted, and the man of war was swift under sail. Equiano's thoughts raced ahead. Could they conceal themselves in the ship and escape capture? Their best chance was below deck.

He motioned to Richard and they quickly scaled the ladder. At the stern were some chests. Richard

hid behind one while Equiano made for the hen coops. He put a finger to his lips. They must not make a sound.

Then it started to rain, not just the usual rain that slanted down and was harmless enough but rain that thumped hard against the deck and pinged off the beams.

Suddenly, the ship juddered. The coops began to lurch. At any moment the coop Equiano was hiding behind would overturn and most probably he would go with it.

The press gang must surely have come alongside by now. Yes, some of them had boarded. He could hear the sound of muffled shouting overhead. They were getting angry. Probably they weren't too pleased with the cheeky answers they were getting from the crew. The terrible weather didn't help either. A thud of heavy footsteps overhead. They must be searching the ship! He could hear the clink of their swords. It sounded as though they were pulling people out by force.

Silence. Just the rain – thump, thump, thump.

Equiano stayed absolutely still, full of anxiety. Each second felt like a minute, an hour. Nothing. The men must have gone.

But then he could hear feet coming down the ladder. He could hear the squelch of their boots. They were going to search below. They would surely find them!

Equiano felt sick and clammy. His head ached. He felt hot one moment, cold the next. He shuddered. But he knew he must be still.

The voices came nearer. There were shouts of anger and confusion. Sailors' curses. Heavy footsteps coming closer. Equiano's heart turned a somersault.

Chapter 5

Suddenly, the coop was thrown aside. He had been discovered!

Two of the gang quickly seized him and held him up by his heels.

'What have we here?' asked one of them.

'A black hen!' replied the other.

'And what ought we to do with a black hen?'

'Put it back in its cage!'

For a moment, Equiano really did think he was about to be put in with the hens. But the mate came to his assistance and pleaded with the press gang to release him. As they were only after strong men, not little boys, they willingly agreed to let him go. The press gang left and the ship was allowed to continue on its passage to London.

A few hours later they reached the mouth of the River Thames at a place called the Nore, still a long way from London. Many ships of war were anchored there, including the *Roebuck*, his master's own ship. As he was taken aboard, Equiano was spellbound to see so many men and guns. He had always longed to take part in a sea battle. And this seemed to be his big chance.

But for the moment he had to settle for another kind of fighting that he had not bargained for at all. On board there were several boys – black and white – and for entertainment in the evenings, the men paired them up for boxing matches. Equiano had never fought against a white boy before. Nor had he ever had a bloody nose. But he soon would have!

The *Roebuck* sailed to the north of Scotland where they picked up even more soldiers. They chased French ships and seventeen surrendered.

They helped rescue a ship that had gone aground. Equiano had the opportunity of firing the guns. But there was no battle.

When the coast was clear, the two boys were landed on a flat, shingle beach at Deal in Kent. From there, they were brought by wagon to London. Even in winter the city reeked to high heaven. Festering horse dung, tubs of excrement and puddles of slimy vomit unleashed a smell so vile that passers-by were almost knocked off their feet. What must it be like in the height of summer? Luckily for them, the boys never found out as they were soon taken out of the city. Richard went to stay with his relatives, while Pascal took Equiano to Westminster where he was introduced to his cousins, Maynard, Elizabeth Martha and Mary Guerin.

'Come this way! Follow me, young man!'

Her starched petticoats rustled as the elder sister, Miss Elizabeth Martha, took Equiano up a steep flight of stairs to the very top of the house.

'This will be your room,' she said with a warm smile. It was a tiny room, more like a cupboard than a room. But it would be his and his alone. And there was a bed and a little chair.

In the street below, among the horses and carriages, he noticed several other black men and women – mostly butlers and servants in the houses of wealthy families – dressed in fashionable flannel waistcoats and pleated under-bodices. But burnt into their skins might well be the initials of their master or mistress. If they dared to run away they could be returned to their owner, as one might return any other piece of labelled property.

Equiano had longed to see London. But the cold and damp had brought him out in chilblains. They were so painful he could not stand up. So the Guerins sent him to St George's Hospital, about a mile and a half away. For a while, his condition seemed to grow worse. The doctors were worried that his whole leg would be infected with gangrene and they were considering cutting it off when Equiano began to show signs of recovering.

Just as he was about to leave hospital, he developed a fever and a nasty rash. Red spots formed on his tongue, blisters filled with pus broke out all over his body. He had gone down with the dreaded smallpox – one of the biggest killer diseases of the day. Britain experienced epidemics of smallpox every few years and over one in ten people who caught it died. Even if you were not killed by smallpox, all of its victims were left with sometimes hideous pock marks. Some sufferers would try to conceal these under layers of powder and make-up, if they could afford to do so. A few would be fortunate, in that the marks would fade as the years went by.

Equiano was immediately put into isolation in a darkened room – well away from the bad air that was believed to bring the disease – and made to sweat it out. He was given nothing to eat and had leeches applied to his arm to suck out the bad blood. Not surprisingly, far from making him feel better, he began to feel weaker. Around his bed, the face of a doctor came in and out of focus as he battled with his illness and the fever came and went. The doctor expected him to die. Equiano was only twelve years old. And he was scared.

Chapter 6

Fortunately for him, after a few weeks he had sweated out the fever and was able to return to the Guerins in Westminster. But there was no time now to explore London, for no sooner than he had settled again in his little room at the top of the house, he and Richard received a message from Captain Pascal that they were to take themselves down river to the port of Deptford. There, Equiano was put on board Pascal's ship *The Royal George* while Richard had to board the *Preston*. They had been best friends. Now they had to part company. As they hugged each other goodbye, it was anyone's guess what the future would hold for either of them.

The Royal George was the largest ship that Equiano could imagine. So many people – men, women and children – and such large guns. It was a little world of its own. There were even shops and stalls, and tradesmen calling out their wares – just as if it were a street in London.

As he was learning to find his way around, Pascal was promoted to an even larger ship called the *Namur* and the crew was moved across with him. The ship was part of a huge fleet under the command of Vice-Admiral Boscawen that would head for Louisbourg in Canada where the French were laying claim to English land. On board was the head of the English land Forces, General James Wolfe – a humane and very well-liked man.

Equiano was now in high hopes of being involved in a sea-fight. He longed to smell the sulphur of cannon fire. But again he had to wait as the whole fleet was blown off course to the island of Teneriffe.

At length, in the summer of 1758, they arrived at Cape Breton Island off the coast of Canada, and the soldiers were landed. However, the French were ready for them in their trenches along the shore, and just as one of the English lieutenants gave orders to fire, they shot at him. The musket ball shot through his mouth and came out of his cheek. Many were killed on both sides until, at last, the French were forced out of their trenches and pursued into the town.

The English chased the French fleet to Louisbourg. Several ships were set on fire and three burned up completely. Louisbourg was captured. The English ships sailed triumphantly into the harbour, decorated with all kinds of colours, from the topmast to the deck. Guns were fired in celebration as Vice-Admiral Boscawen and his officers came ashore to take possession of the town and fort of Louisbourg in the name of King George of England.

The celebrations were over, and Equiano returned to London where the *Namur* was refitted. Pascal took him back to Westminster, to the Guerin sisters, where else? He felt completely at home there in the company of English people. But if he was ever to really get on he had to be able to read and write. After his separation from Richard he had been able to make very little progress with his education.

In return for doing various odd jobs for the Guerins, they taught him to read and gave him Bible lessons. But the other servants told him that he would never get to heaven unless he was baptized. And so, on 9th February 1759 at St Margaret's Church in Westminster, Equiano was baptized, with the elder sister, Miss Elizabeth Martha and her brother, Maynard, acting as his godparents. When the ceremony was over, the balding clerk filled in the register. Equiano was recorded as 'Gustavus Vassa.' The clerk asked him where he was born and he replied 'Carolina' in the USA, not Africa. Why did he say this? Is it possible that he had made up the whole story of his childhood in Africa, his kidnap and his horrific journey by ship to the West Indies?

Chapter 7

After two months the *Namur* had finished its refit and Equiano was ordered on board. In recognition of his loyal service, Pascal promoted him to the rank of able seaman. He did not want to leave London and go to sea right now; the Guerin sisters had been so kind to him, and he did not want to give up school. But he had no choice.

After eleven days they passed the southernmost tip of Spain and reached Gibraltar, a country owned by England. There he told people his story – how, many years ago in Africa, he and his sister had been kidnapped. After one telling, a man said that he believed he knew where his sister was. Full of hope, Equiano followed him to the house of a black woman. She was so like his sister that at first he believed it really was her. But as soon as he spoke to her, his hopes were dashed. She came from another country altogether.

As if that wasn't disappointing enough, more bad news was to follow while he was in Gibraltar. Richard Baker's ship came in and he ran to the dock to meet up with his old friend. The crew told him that Richard was dead. Like Equiano, he had caught the smallpox, but unlike him had not survived. The crew had thrown his body overboard so as to prevent the spread of infection. All they had was his small chest of belongings – containing a few clothes and books, nothing of value. They handed it over to him. Equiano said nothing. He went below deck, took out his Bible and began to talk to it. He had always thought of Richard as a brother, one of his own brothers back in Africa. And thinking of Africa made him long for his mother.

But there was little time for grief. A few nights

later, they sighted the French fleet off the coast of Gibraltar, and at four o'clock the next afternoon they caught up with it. Their instructions were to attack the Commander's ship, which was called *Ocean*. They fired all three tiers of guns at her at once. The *Ocean* returned fire.

During the engagement Equiano worked as a 'powder monkey', bringing gunpowder to the guns on the middle deck. It was all very dangerous. The powder was kept deep down in the ship's hull. To reach it he had to run nearly the whole length of the ship. It was very slippery because they had run out of sand to sprinkle over the deck. As he ran, he was exposed to enemy shots. What made matters worse was that the bottoms of the boxes carrying the cartridges full of gunpowder were rotten and powder leaked onto the deck close to the fire.

The fighting went on and on. Commands were bellowed out but many were not properly heard above the deafening cannon fire. At times he couldn't bear it any longer and would put his hands over his ears. (Was it really him, just a few years

earlier that had yearned for a sea battle? How he had changed). Flying splinters left the sailors with terrible injuries. Pascal himself was wounded and was taken down to the surgeon. The guns thundered away, the air stank with the acrid smoke of gunpowder.

Eventually, the French line was broken. The English gave chase. The *Ocean* and another French ship called the *Redoubtable* ran aground, and the English set fire to both of them. There was a terrible explosion, and the midnight sky was so bright it seemed that day had dawned early. Equiano's own ship, the *Namur*, was badly damaged in the engagement, the rigging was shattered and a mast was down and hanging over the deck.

As soon as Pascal had recovered from his injuries, he was made captain of a small ship called the *Aetna* and Equiano was transferred with him. He was promoted, too. No longer was Equiano a powder monkey; he now became the captain's steward. He loved it on the *Aetna*. A man called Daniel Queen taught him how to shave and cut the captain's hair.

They became good friends and in the evenings Queen would help Equiano read his Bible.

But life was still just as risky for him, and he had two very lucky escapes. The first was when he fell headlong from the upper deck. Everyone expected him to be killed instantly but, miraculously, he wasn't in the slightest bit injured. The second was at Belle Isle, off the west coast of France, when a French shell exploded just a few yards from him but he managed to dive under a big rock. How had he managed to survive? His only explanation was that God had saved him.

When summer came, the English captured Belle Isle, and by November the war that had raged for seven long years since 1756 was over. People were talking about peace.

Shortly before Christmas they sailed up the Thames and cast anchor at Deptford. Equiano was looking forward to being paid his wages and his prize-money. He was also expecting a bit of shore leave.

'Don't think you're leaving me because you're not!' shouted Pascal.

'Please sir.' Equiano's voice was strange. High and squeaky. He began again. 'Please sir, may I go for my books and my chest?'

'No! You may not! How dare you! If you move out of my sight, I'll slit your throat!'

'But sir. You *cannot* treat me like this!'

As he looked up, he noticed how the gold lacing on the captain's uniform had turned green from sea salt.

Pascal cracked his knuckles.

'I'll be the one to decide how I'll treat you!'

With that, he pushed Equiano into a barge. He was taken down river towards Gravesend. There they came alongside a ship called the *Charming Sally* that was bound for the West Indies. Pascal went on board, ordering Equiano to wait, and again threatening to slit his throat if he moved.

After a while, the captain of the *Charming Sally*, whose name was James Doran, sent for him in his cabin.

'You are now *my* slave,' he told Equiano in a matter of fact tone.

'But I am not for sale.'

'What do you mean, boy? Didn't your master buy you?' Doran glanced across at Pascal.

'But he is my master. I have served him many years.'

'Yes, and now you will be able to serve me for many years, too – in the West Indies!'

'But I've been baptized…'

Doran threw his head back and laughed. 'Poppycock!' he roared.

'Sir, by the laws of the land no man has a right to sell me. I heard a lawyer tell my master so.'

Doran stopped laughing and looked Equiano straight in the eye. 'You talk too much English. If you don't behave yourself and be quiet, I have a method on board to make you.'

Equiano did not doubt what he said. He knew only too well the kind of torture instruments used in the slave ships and shuddered at the thought. There was no point in arguing.

And sure enough he was sold there and then in Gravesend – just as if he was a bag of rice. And

what was worse, Pascal refused to pay him any of
the prize money he had won. He even took away
his coat and books – including his precious Bible
and Richard's *Life of Christopher Columbus*. All he
was left with in the whole world was nine guineas,
which he thought he had better hide in case his
master should get his thieving hands on that as well.

Equiano was full of bitterness. He had been used
and cheated. There he was. Seventeen years old. He
had been fighting for the English for almost half his
young life. Now that the war was over he expected
to be given his freedom and to receive a cut in the
spoils of victory. Why was he being punished like
this? It *had* to be because his skin was black.

Chapter 8

'…and now you will serve me for many years, too – in the West Indies!' Captain Doran's words were still ringing in his ears. He would be returning to where he had begun his existence as a slave seven years earlier. It would be like going back to square one.

The *Charming Sally* sailed to Portsmouth on the south coast of England where they prepared for the voyage to the West Indies. The very thought of returning to a place where Africans were so brutally treated filled him with horror and he begged the crew to help him escape. In return for a guinea, one of them agreed to get him a boat. But he never saw his guinea, the promised boat, or even the man again. His old shipmates had also promised help but only sent him a crate of oranges. Miss Elizabeth Martha Guerin sent him a letter promising to get him off the ship but it was all too late. They had set sail and Equiano felt only hopelessness and despair. His fate already seemed decided and he was powerless to do anything about it. He cursed the tide, the wind and the ship itself, and called on death to end it all.

The sea stayed smooth and after six weeks they came within sight of the Caribbean island of Montserrat. He sensed black clouds gathering above him. He knew that ahead of him would be years of misery, in chains, on a plantation.

As he helped unload the ship, two sailors approached him and engaged him in conversation. While one was asking for directions, the other one, unbeknown to Equiano, was helping himself to the slave's purse which could be seen poking out of his pocket. One of them gave him a push and he fell to the ground, while the pair of them made their escape with his precious nine guineas.

A few mornings later he feared more bad news when Captain Doran summoned him to his cabin. Seated opposite him was a stout man in a black cape and a tall black hat, the brim of which came down over his face.

'I am returning to London' said Doran.

Equiano's eyes rested on a map that lay on the captain's table.

'May I return with you, sir?'

'No. I have a new master for you – the very best master in the whole of the island. He is a Quaker by religion. You will be as happy with him as if you were in England...'

'But I would like to be in England, sir!'

'Quiet! Let me introduce you to Mr Robert King. He does not come from these parts, his home being in Philadelphia, not far from New York. Look, here. [He pointed a stubby finger at the map]. You will return there with him soon.'

King looked across at Equiano with a friendly

smile. 'What can you offer?'

'I know a little about seamanship, I can shave and dress hair, I can write.

And I know a little arithmetic.'

'What about navigation?'

'Why, no.'

'Not to worry. One of my clerks will teach you.'

Equiano was duly taught what he needed to know about plotting routes and steering a ship – skills which many a master would never have dared teach a slave for fear they would use their knowledge to escape. So that over the next year King was able to send Equiano to different parts of Montserrat to collect rum and sugar. He also sent him to trade with the neighbouring islands of St Kitts and St Eustatia.

It was while he was in St Kitts one day that a very strange thing happened. A white man wanted to marry a free black woman who had land and slaves on Montserrat. But the clergyman had told the couple that the law forbade a black to marry a white in church. After much pleading he agreed to

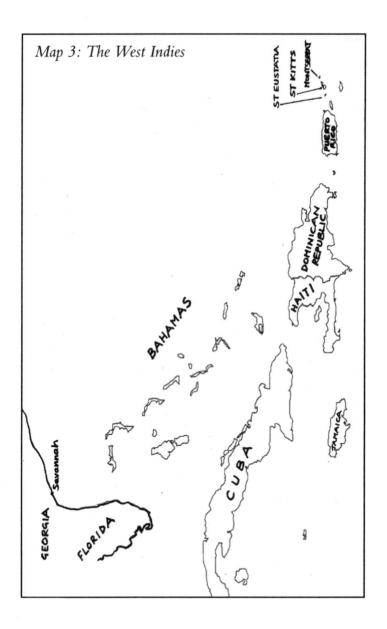

Map 3: The West Indies

ST EUSTATIA

ST KITTS

MONTSERRAT

PUERTO RICO

DOMINICAN REPUBLIC

HAITI

BAHAMAS

JAMAICA

GEORGIA

Savannah

FLORIDA

CUBA

marry them on the water. So the couple went in one boat and the clergyman and the clerk in another boat, and the ceremony was performed out at sea! Equiano was very happy that they had succeeded. He dreamed that one day he might find a woman he could love. What would it matter if she were white? Why should the law make it so difficult for a black person to marry a white?

In St Eustatia he decided to see just how good a merchant he would make. As he only had three pence, it was a risky business! He spent the three pence on a glass tumbler from a trader. When he reached Montserrat he sold the tumbler for sixpence. So, on the next trip he took the sixpence, bought another two tumblers, and sold them on Montserrat for double – a shilling. He continued buying and selling like this until, within a month, he had made a dollar. It had to be the fastest buck ever to be made by a slave!

In return for allowing Equiano to move about like this, Mr King expected him to work hard – up to sixteen hours a day. As well as collecting rum and sugar, he stood in as a clerk. He received and delivered ships' cargoes, looked after the stores, shaved and dressed his master and tended to his horse. King reckoned that he saved £100 each year by having Equiano do these things for him. So no wonder he always refused to sell him.

In fairness, King deserved his good reputation. He was kind and humane and fed his slaves well. He also knew that they would be happier and would work better that way. If any of his slaves misbehaved he would never put iron muzzles and thumb screws on them, nor flog them as other masters did; he simply sold them on to someone else.

How different was King to the vast majority of slave owners. They would begin their cruelties at sea by turning the ship into a prison from which they could not escape. When some slaves managed to jump clear of the net around their ship, one captain had his men go after them in a boat and bring back their dead bodies. The captain then grabbed a meat cleaver and cut the heads off their bodies.

'If they believe they are going back to Africa it will be without their heads!' he told the rest of the slaves, gleefully.

When they reached the plantations, work was tough – planting crops and cutting sugar cane during the day, and working in the boiling house all night. Any slacking or carelessness or lateness would be punished with the whip. Some masters would then literally 'rub salt' (or pepper) into their wounds. Or the slaves might be made to turn a treadmill, and whipped if they did not keep up to speed.

Some tried to run away, but if they were caught, iron rings were snapped around their ankles and pothooks fastened around their necks. One Negro man called Emanuel Sankey tried to escape by hiding on a ship bound for London. He was discovered and taken to his master who pinned his wrists and ankles to the deck, took some sticks of sealing wax, lit them and dropped the hot wax all over his back.

Another overseer punished his slaves by shutting

them up in a long wooden box like a coffin. There were holes in the box to let in a little air, as the owner did not want the slave to die – merely to suffer.

When, eventually, he was released he would be in a terrible state – dehydrated, staggering to his feet, blinking furiously in the daylight.

Outside of King's supervision, Equiano was exposed every day to hardship and cheating. He was sworn at, molested and robbed in every one of the islands – and he visited fifteen in the West Indies. But there was no point in a black person taking a white person to court because no black person was allowed to give evidence against a white person. In the eyes of the law black people were inferior.

It was not that the slave dealers had been born any worse than other men. Equiano believed that if they had taken up a different trade they might have stayed as tender-hearted and generous as the day they were born. But they had been so badly corrupted by greed that they had become unfeeling and cruel. These feelings had poisoned their minds and the minds of their families – spreading like a terrible disease.

He dreamed of being a free man in England where he would be safe! Pray that might be the future which God had mapped out for him. He had to make every effort to obtain his freedom. By continuing to improve his knowledge of navigation, he might be able to escape. So he paid the mate what little money he had to give him lessons.

As his knowledge grew, his skills became more and more in demand, and one of King's captains who was known for his fairness, Thomas Farmer, asked permission to recruit Equiano as a sailor. The swarthy-skinned Farmer explained to King how Equiano was more useful than three white men who tended to get drunk so as to avoid work. But King was worried that his precious slave might run away, and he took some persuading before he let Equiano go. Even then it was on condition that if he did run away, Farmer would have to pay for him.

As it turned out, King's fears were unfounded,

and a few months later Equiano was safely back on the east coast of America, in his master's home town of Philadelphia with its neatly laid out streets and elegant houses. There he was told of a wise woman, a Mrs Davis, who could predict the future. Equiano was doubtful, as he had grown up to believe that no human being could foresee what God had planned.

One night Mrs Davis appeared in a dream. This made him change his ideas. He was now anxious to meet her and was shown where she lived. Astonishingly, the woman was wearing the very same dress as in his dream! In her back parlour she told him that she had one good piece of news and one bad piece. The good piece was that he would not be a slave for very much longer. The bad news was that before he gained his freedom he would twice be in very great danger of his life.

Chapter 9

King moved to his plantations in Savannah, Georgia, at the beginning of 1765 and took all his slaves with him. Overworked and run down from his long hours rowing between the islands, Equiano soon caught a bad fever and chill. For eleven days he was confined to bed, very ill. At one point it looked as though he might die. Perhaps there was something to be said for fortune-tellers. It certainly looked as though the wise woman's first prediction had come true.

Then, one Sunday night, when Equiano was hanging around with some Negroes, their master, whose name was Dr Perkins, came in drunk. Not liking to see any strange Negroes in his yard, he and another white man struck Equiano with the first weapons they could get hold of. Dr Perkins grabbed a large spade and whacked Equiano around the head, throwing him off balance. The other man got hold of a sharp axe and started to attack Equiano with it. He suffered so many cuts that blood was gushing forth. At the sight of all his injuries the two men became alarmed. They did not want to kill him, just punish him, as he had no business being there. But Equiano had lost consciousness.

The next morning when he opened his eyes, he found himself in jail. The two men must have carried him there during the night. When his captain found out what had happened he managed to use his influence to get Equiano out of jail and immediately sent for the best doctors. At first they thought they could do nothing to save him. But thanks to the good medical skills of a Dr Brady, Equiano began to recover. But he had been in danger of his life once again. Remarkably, the wise woman's second prediction had come true.

Two weeks later he was able to get out of bed, which was just as well because the captain was ready to return to Montserrat in the West Indies.

As the vessel was being loaded, an elderly man approached the ship. The poor man, a silversmith by trade, was so desperate to return to his lands in the West Indies that he agreed to pay the captain a lot of money. But just as the vessel was about to set sail, the silversmith was suddenly taken ill. The captain asked Equiano to help watch over him at night, and promised him ten pounds for doing so. Equiano was so pleased that he went out straight away and spent eight pounds of it on a wonderful blue suit. He decided to put it away safely so that he could wear it to dance in on the day he got his freedom.

The captain and Equiano attended the silversmith dutifully – day as well as night – but he grew worse. As he had no wife or children, he promised to give the captain all he had when he died.

A few days later, at two in the morning, the

captain was told that the silversmith was dead. He went and woke Equiano.

'Get up and get a light. Come with me immediately!'

Equiano was very sleepy and wanted to wait until morning.

'No, no,' said the captain. 'We will have the money tonight. I cannot wait till tomorrow; let's go now!'

So Equiano got up and struck a light.

When they reached the dead man's cabin he was as dead as they could have wished, so they started to search through all his belongings. In a corner of his cabin was a large trunk. The captain snapped open the lock and looked inside. To his surprise he saw another trunk. Opening this he found another! The captain opened one after another. Each one had another inside it, rather like Russian dolls. What might be in the very last trunk that the silversmith so wanted to conceal? It was all very exciting.

But soon, excitement turned to despair. All they found was a sheaf of papers and one and a half

dollars. Not even enough to pay for the man's coffin! Equiano's voice failed him. For once he was speechless. They had taken such good care of the man when he was alive. And he had cheated them! Could he ever trust a white man again?

Chapter 10

Robert King's house in Montserrat

'Give you your freedom?'

'Yes sir. You did promise…'

'But do you have forty pounds to buy it?'

Robert King tilted his head. His hat seemed to have grown even bigger than when he saw him last, and for a moment Equiano thought that it was going to topple off! He looked up at Equiano doubtfully.

'Yes sir.'

'Where on earth did you get the money from?'

'Very honestly, sir.'

King glanced across at Captain Farmer.

'There is no doubt that he has got his money honestly, through hard work,' said Farmer. Equiano knew that he could trust Captain Farmer to speak well on his behalf. He was a good man.

King puffed out his chest. Out of the tall sash windows that lined his grand living room, the largest on the island, he could see in the distance a ship (one of his ships) being loaded with sugar. 'He seems to earn money faster than I can! I would not have promised him his freedom if I had realised that he was going to claim it this quickly!'

'Come, come Robert,' said Farmer, slapping him on the back. 'I think you must let him have his freedom. 'He has done well for you. He's earned you more than a hundred a year. And he will still save you money as he will not leave you even when he is free.'

'Very well. I did make a promise, so I shall stick to it. Any promise from a Quaker is as binding as if it had been sworn on the Bible.'

He leant across, took the forty pounds, and told Equiano to go to the Register Office and get the necessary freedom papers drawn up.

Equiano repeated his master's words over and over again. 'I did make a promise, so I shall stick to it...' They were like a voice from heaven. His eyes filled with tears. As he ran to the Register Office his feet scarcely touched the ground. There, the Registrar was so pleased for him that he drew up the papers for a guinea, which was half the normal price.

Equiano could now read the words Robert King had said a few hours earlier:

'that a negro man slave, named Gustavus Vassa shall become free...'

His eyes shone. His existence as a slave was over! He could not believe it. He was free at last! It was the happiest day of his life. He was twenty-one years old and a free man. Equiano ran straight back to his master so he could sign it and make it all legal. Now he had to guard that piece of paper with his life. It would be his only proof that he had his freedom.

That night he celebrated his freedom by inviting all his friends to a party, and he danced in the blue suit that he had bought in Georgia especially for the occasion – an occasion that he was beginning to think might never arrive.

In the streets of Montserrat white and black people called him 'freeman'. For Equiano, it was the most special name in the whole world. What would his old master, Captain Pascal, have thought if he had seen him, no longer a planter's slave but a free man.

But would his new-found freedom be all that he had hoped for?

Chapter 11

Mr King took off his huge hat and looked Equiano straight in the eyes. 'You won't leave me now you are free, will you?'

Equiano reflected, but only for a moment: 'No sir!'

He could not let his master down for he had been good to him, the kindest master he had ever had. So, he agreed to go on board ship again with Captain Farmer and to serve as an able bodied seaman.

They sailed to St Eustatia, collected rum and sugar, and brought it back to Savannah, Georgia.

They found it hard to carry it ashore as the river was full of alligators that kept trying to get into the boats. But there were other problems too.

One day a slave owned by a Mr Read came up to the ship and started jeering and insulting Equiano. No matter how many times he asked him to stop, he just kept doing it. Jealousy, he supposed – he must have known that Equiano was a free man. When the slave punched him in the face, Equiano could not stop himself giving the slave a good beating in return.

The next morning, while Captain Farmer was ashore, Mr Read, an ugly man, showed up at the ship waving a stick.

'I'll have you flogged publicly through every street in Savannah for beating my slave!' he roared.

Equiano explained that the slave had insulted him and had punched him first.

'I want to see the captain!' he fumed.

'He's not here. He's in town on business,' replied Equiano.

Read spat on the ground in frustration and left.

But later he came back. By then, Captain Farmer was back and Read asked him to hand Equiano over.

The captain refused, saying that Equiano was a free man.

Read went off a second time, threatening to return with constables to arrest him.

Farmer told Equiano to leave the ship and hide on the outskirts of Savannah where he had his board and lodging. In the meantime he tracked down Read. He told him how much he needed Equiano on the ship and begged him not to do anything to him.

Read soon got very tired of all Farmer's talk and gave in so as to get rid of him. His parting words were 'He can go to Hell for all I care.'

Now safe, Equiano went back on board ship where he was given the task of loading oxen for sale in the West Indies. As the animals were being herded on, one ox charged at the captain and gave him such a nasty head butt in the chest that he became too dizzy to steer the ship. What made matters worse was that the mate was also sick, so Equiano had to work harder than ever. In return, Farmer promised to let him take two bulls of his own aboard. He reckoned he would be able to sell them when they reached Montserrat.

But when the captain was feeling better he went back on his word. Equiano was disappointed. He had hoped to make a lot of money. Seeing how upset he was, Farmer had a twinge of guilt and suggested that he bring some turkeys on board instead. Equiano was not sure the birds would be strong enough to survive a sea journey but the captain insisted, and Equiano went off to buy four dozen. All of them joined the ship's cat on board. The men had never bothered to give the cat a name. To them, it was there for one purpose only which was to catch rats in the ship's hold where the stores were kept. They did not look upon it as a pet. It was there to do a job of work, like them.

Eventually they sailed for Montserrat. The mate was still sick and the captain had not recovered from the ox's blow. And as the days passed, they both grew worse – so bad that neither of them was fit to navigate. So Equiano was put in charge of the ship. He did his best, using what he could remember from his lessons in navigation.

Soon, Captain Farmer was so sick that he could not even get out of bed. Realizing that he had not much longer to live, he called Equiano to his cabin. The captain was in bed, looking extremely pale.

'Have I ever done you any harm?' His voice was feeble, barely audible.

'God forbid I should ever think so! You have done so much to help me!' replied Equiano.

The poor captain died without uttering another word.

Equiano took out his Bible and talked to it. He would now have to steer the ship himself.

After nine days of bad weather, the ship reached Antigua, one of the Leeward Islands. He thanked God, without whose help he believed he never would have succeeded in steering a safe course. The day after that they arrived safely at Montserrat where he was greeted this time not as freeman but as captain. All the oxen had died but every one of Equiano's turkeys had survived, and he went on to sell them at 300 per cent profit!

He smiled. Now he was surely free to sail for England as a free man. But Robert King was unwilling to let him go and begged Equiano to make one more voyage for him. Out of loyalty, he agreed to do it. And so, under the command of a new captain, William Phillips, they sailed in the *Nancy* for Georgia.

Phillips turned out to be a bit of an odd-ball. He was also a right old show off, claiming that what he didn't know about navigation wasn't worth knowing. Surprising then that he steered such a peculiar course – much further to the west than any helmsman Equiano had ever seen before!

That night Equiano had a nightmare. The ship was being dashed against rocks. As if that was not bad enough, he was being held responsible for saving everyone on board.

The next night he had the same dream. As he tried to put the dream out of his mind, things started to go very wrong.

The evening afterwards, as he was pumping water out of the ship, he could see that it was badly leaking.

'Curses!' he exclaimed.

The words had slipped out before he knew it. The sailors would think nothing of cursing and blinding the whole day through but Equiano knew that swearing was sinful. Feeling ashamed, he left the deck and went below to pray for forgiveness and then to bed.

Almost at once he had the same dream again. He got up and went back on deck.

At half past one in the morning the man at the helm shouted out to him that the ship had washed against a dolphin.

Equiano took a close look.

'It's not a dolphin. It's a rock!'

The sea was sweeping angrily against it, over and over again.

He rushed down to warn the captain.

'No need to worry!' said Phillips. He turned in

his bed and went fast to sleep again.

When Equiano got back on deck, the current was taking hold of the ship and carrying it towards the rock. So he went down to the captain again and told him that he *had* to come up on deck immediately, that there were breakers all around them.

When the captain still did not appear, Equiano ran down to him a third time.

Eventually he emerged and gave the crew instructions to lower the anchor.

But before they had a chance to do so there was a thud, then an awful wrenching sound.

Chapter 12

The ship had struck the rock. The hull had been pierced. Equiano was convinced that God was punishing him for swearing and that they would all drown. And – just as in his dream – he would be responsible.

Captain Phillips was in a right old panic. 'Nail down the hatches!'

The crew got themselves ready to carry out his command. Equiano could not believe what he was hearing. 'Stop! There are twenty slaves in the hold. If you do that they will all die!'

'It's got to be done!' said the captain.

'Why?'

'Because if we let them up they will all try to get into the boat and it can only carry ten. They'll end up drowning.'

'You're the one who deserves to drown!' bellowed Equiano. 'It's all your fault this has happened. You aren't a captain. You've got no idea how to steer a ship!'

The crew was stunned by Equiano's brave words – the words of a man who recognized the slaves they carried were human beings and not just cargo. The captain knew at once that he would have a mutiny on his hands if he made the crew carry out his orders. No one nailed down any hatches that day.

'We must get the boat ready for the morning,' ordered Equiano.

The crew needed no further persuading and every one of them came across to his aid. But there was a hole in the bottom of the boat and there was nothing to mend it with. So he took some leather from one of the pumps and nailed it over the hole.

Then began the long wait until daylight.

When dawn broke they noticed that about five miles away lay a small island. Dangerous reefs seemed to surround it – but somehow they knew they must get there.

As they drew close to the island they thought they could see people. The captain was convinced they were cannibals, that it would be safer to find somewhere else to land. Then, to their relief, they walked off. The crew had been deceived by the sun's reflection. It turned out they were not even humans (let alone cannibals) but flamingos. They saw them fly away!

The crew went back and forth from the ship to the island five times. In the final trip they took the cat with them. None of the white men helped, they had completely given up and were lying flat out drunk on the deck, like pigs. In fact, they were so drunk that they had to be lifted by force into the boat; otherwise they would have died. Fortunately, every one of the thirty-two people on board was saved. Equiano knew that it had been his duty to save them. If he had failed, God would have held him responsible.

Now on shore, they used the ship's sails to make tents to live in. After this they repaired the boat. It was a lengthy process but in eleven days it was ready. During that time the ship's cat had disappeared. The unaccustomed freedom had led it to wander off into the woodland, never to be seen again. To his surprise, Equiano actually felt quite sad at its loss.

The captain, Equiano and five others set off in the hope of reaching New Providence in the Bahamas. All they had in the way of rations was rum, a little water, salt beef and some ship's biscuits that were like hard rusks.

After two days they reached Abaco, the largest of the Bahamas. But they had run out of water. They searched everywhere. One of the sailors even lapped up water from the leaves of shrubs.

Just as they were starting to despair, the captain cried out 'A sail! A sail!'

They launched the boat and set off towards the

sail. As they drew closer they could see a boat full of people. At first they believed they might be pirates but it turned out that they, too, had been shipwrecked and were very friendly. A deal was struck. If they agreed to rescue Captain Phillips and his crew, in return they could take anything of value they wished from the wreck of the *Nancy*.

And so this is how they reached New Providence. There, Phillips was able to hire a ship to take them to Savannah, Georgia, which they reached safely. Equiano might have guessed he would have further problems in Georgia! And sure enough he did have. A few evenings after their arrival, he was at the house of a black friend. It was between nine and ten o'clock, they had finished dinner, had lit a lamp and were sitting around talking. As the night patrol was passing they saw the light and knocked at the door. They were welcomed in, sat down, and even shared a bowl of punch with them.

Suddenly one of them got up.

'You are to come to the watch house with us!'

No one moved.

'At once!'

Equiano was speechless.

'Any Negro who shows a light in their house after nine o'clock is to be fined or flogged.'

They tied Equiano's hands and took him to the watch house.

Chapter 13

It was only due to the intervention of his friend Dr Brady – the one who had saved him from the wise woman's illness – that he was spared a flogging.

Equiano needed no further incentive to leave Georgia. Disgusted by his treatment there, he wished it 'good riddance,' and was determined never, ever, to return.

Seven weeks later he arrived back in London at Cherry Garden Stairs, a landing place that stunk of herrings and mouldy oranges on the south bank of the Thames, about four miles from Westminster. He was paid his wages of seven guineas (this gave him thirty-seven guineas in all) and headed off towards where the Guerin sisters lived. How he was looking forward to telling them stories of how he had fought in battle, been tricked and cheated, and twice nearly died. But it turned out that these stories would have to wait as the sisters had moved out of London to the fresher airs of Greenwich in Kent.

Close by where they lived in May's Hill is Greenwich Park, and who should Equiano find strolling along in the park but their cousin, Captain Pascal. When he saw his former slave his eyes almost popped out of his head.

'What are you doing here? How the devil did you get back?'

'Why, in a ship!' said Equiano with a smirk.

Pascal looked down at him.

'Well, I assumed you did not walk back to London on the water.'

As he strode off through the park, cane in hand, he did not appear to be in the least sorry for how he had treated him.

A few days later he met him again, this time at the Guerins' house. Now there was more time to speak. And what an opportunity to show him up in front of his cousins! Equiano promptly asked Pascal for his prize money.

'Prize money? What prize money? There is none due to you.'

'What?'

'As a matter of fact, even if you had prize money of £10,000 I would still have a right to it all.'

'But I've been told…'

'Start a law suit against me if you wish.'

'I might do just that.'

Pascal cracked his knuckles loudly and stormed out.

When he had gone, the sisters sat Equiano down. They explained to him that they would like to have taken him on as a servant but could not afford to do so. Miss Elizabeth Martha asked him whether there was anything else they could do for him.

Equiano thought for a moment.

'Could you recommend me to someone who

could teach me a business so that I might earn a living?'

'What business would you like to learn?' asked Miss Mary.

'Hair dressing,' he answered decisively.

So they recommended him to a hairdresser in Haymarket, in the West End of London. There he was trained how to curl the hair of young ladies and to powder the wigs of fashionable young gentlemen. How he would have loved to be an English gentleman!

In the same courtyard was a clergyman, called the Reverend Mr Gregory, who kept a school. Equiano would go there some evenings to brush up his arithmetic. He also paid a neighbour to teach him to play the French horn, which helped pass the long winter evenings.

But his job with the hairdresser did not work out, and the following February he went to live with Dr Charles Irving close by in Pall Mall. Irving, a rather timid and private man, was famous for his experiments to purify sea water so that it was fresh

enough to drink. He was also trying to discover a way of keeping meat fresh on long sea voyages but had not yet been successful.

Irving was very kind and good-tempered, and allowed Equiano to carry on with his hairdressing and arithmetic lessons. But his wages were much less than before (just £12 a year), and he had to dip into his savings. Before long his thirty-seven guineas had become just one guinea. He was almost broke! So he again decided to try the sea, from which he had made such a good living before.

Over the next few years Equiano earned a living from dressing hair overseas. He sailed to Oporto in Portugal, arriving during carnival time. He travelled to Naples in Italy where he witnessed at close hand the eruption of Mount Vesuvius. While he was in the Turkish city of Smyrna he struck up a friendship with an officer who offered him two wives if he stayed. But he resisted the temptation. He told him that one wife was as much as most men could manage, and that some could not even manage one!

Having run out of places of interest in Europe, in

1771 he decided to try his fortune again in the West Indies. This was very nearly the end of Equiano. Aboard ship one evening, while he was writing up his journal in the storeroom where he slept, he absentmindedly rested his candle on a box of hemp fibre. The flame made contact with one of the threads and in an instant the whole lot was ablaze. His shirt caught fire, so did the handkerchief around his neck. The smoke was choking him. He shouted for help. He thought that his time had come, that he would perish in the flames. Fortunately, the crew was close by and came with blankets and mattresses to smother the fire. In a short while it was out, and Equiano was let off with a severe reprimand. After this he returned to London.

But soon he was longing to go to sea again. So he prowled the streets close to where the ships were docked in the Thames, asking every captain, quartermaster and sailor where they were sailing. To his great excitement he heard news that an expedition was being planned to discover a sea route to India – via the North Pole! Two ships were involved – the *Racehorse* and the *Carcass*. Equiano is recorded as 'Gustavus Weston' on the muster list of the *Racehorse* . He told the ship's clerk the same as he had told the clerk at St Margaret's Church in Westminster – that his place of birth was South Carolina.

Also signing up to board the *Carcass* was the future great naval hero, Horatio Nelson, then aged just fourteen.

Although they did not find a new route to India, it was a truly magical voyage, full of spectacular surroundings – all frozen in the intense cold. Equiano saw Greenland where the sun did not set; he caught sight of walruses and whales between the icebergs; and he even tasted polar bear (which he did not like, he found the meat tough!). His special responsibility on board was to provide fresh drinking water using Dr Irving's apparatus, and he managed to distil up to forty gallons of seawater a day!

When he returned to London he thanked God that he had got safely home. He started going to church – St James' in Piccadilly, St Martin-in-the-Fields and St Anne's, Soho. But the services bored him. So he 'shopped around.' He tried going to a Quaker meeting house where everything was done in silence. But that did not inspire him. He investigated the Roman Catholic and Jewish religions but they had no better effect on him. He got more out of reading his Bible at home than going to church. He was so fed up that he planned to go back to Turkey. The Turks seemed to have better morals than those who called themselves Christians in Europe. He was ready to set sail from London on Easter Monday when something suddenly happened that was to change the course of the rest of his life.

A man called William Kirkpatrick suddenly showed up at the ship, as if out of nowhere. Head in the air, strutting along, cane in hand. All while the six men he had brought with him were routing out the ship's cook, whose name was John Annis. For many years, Annis had worked for Kirkpatrick in St Kitts in the West Indies. Although they had parted by consent, Kirkpatrick had made several attempts to kidnap his former slave.

Equiano grabbed hold of Kirkpatrick's collar. The slaver reeled and kicked out at him.

'Take your filthy black hands off me! Just who the hell do you think you are?'

'I am a friend of John Annis. He is a free man. You have no claim on him.'

Kirkpatrick's red face became crimson.

'I'll be the judge of that you nigger!'

Kirkpatrick beckoned to his men to tie Annis up and take him away. With a mean glance behind at Equiano, he swaggered off.

Chapter 14

Equiano was incensed, and over the next few months he made every effort to get Kirkpatrick caught. On one occasion he even whitened his face so that he could go to his house in St Paul's Church yard undetected. But his attempts failed. So he decided to see Granville Sharp. He had read that he was a great champion of the rights of slaves.

Sharp – or 'Greeny' as he was known to his friends – had got involved in the campaign against the slave trade purely by chance. One afternoon back in 1765, when he was only thirty years old (he was now fifty), Sharp had been visiting his brother

William, who was a doctor in Mincing Lane in the City of London. As he left, and began to thread his way through the throngs of pie sellers, flower girls and beggars, he suddenly caught sight of a Negro man of about sixteen or seventeen years old whose face was badly bleeding. He was standing in a long queue to see William, who gave free medical help to the poor. Granville was so distressed by his appearance that he stopped and examined him more closely. The poor man had hardly anything left of his face, and what was left had been reduced to a crimson pulp. He took the man into the surgery where he told them that his name was Jonathan Strong. As William dressed his wounds and washed his eyes, Strong told him that his master was a West Indian planter called David Lisle who had brought him from Barbados to England on a visit. After he had had too much to drink one day, Lisle had lost his temper and had savagely beaten him with the butt of his pistol. Half-blinded and scarcely able to walk, he had been thrown into the street as if for dead. His injuries were so bad that the brothers took him to St Bartholomew's Hospital where he remained for four and a half months. They paid for his clothes while he was in there, and when he came out found him a lodging, and gave him some money so he could get back on his feet again. When he had improved (he was still lame and he never recovered his sight) he got a job as an apothecary's messenger.

All went well until two years later when, quite by chance, he came across David Lisle again. His old master was furious! After all, he had chucked him into the street as a good-for-nothing. But here he was – right in front of his very eyes. If only he had kept him he could have made some money out of him! After all, he was obviously capable of work. His anger began to well up inside him. A few days later he was so angry that he hired two men to capture Jonathan Strong and take him to prison. From here he would be shipped off to a planter in Jamaica and Lisle would earn himself a nice fat £30 in the sale.

But while he was in prison, Strong managed to

smuggle a message to Granville Sharp, pleading for his help. What could Sharp do? The law was confused about whether or not a West Indian slave living in England was free or not. Sharp's lawyer advised him that there were good grounds for thinking that slaves remained as slaves in this country. Strong's new master threatened to sue Sharp for loss of property. Meanwhile his old master challenged Sharp to a duel! The poor man was getting it in the neck from both sides.

Eventually Strong was released. After all, the lad had not stolen anything and was not guilty of any offence. In 1772 Sharp helped get a law passed that said that slaves brought to England could not be forced back to slavery in the colonies.

It was now 1774. The law was now clear. The Annis episode should never have happened. When Equiano had finished his story, Sharp told him that he must go to see a lawyer. There was surely every hope of getting Annis his freedom back. But the lawyer, as so many others had done in Equiano's life, took his money and did nothing. And when

Annis arrived in St Kitts he was forced into slavery again. His wrists and ankles were staked to the ground, he was flogged and irons were put around his neck.

The incident made Equiano determined to pray extra hard to God. He even started to take his Bible with him when he went out. And as he was reading and talking to it one day he got into conversation with an old sailor who introduced him to a Methodist minister. He had briefly seen a Methodist church in Savannah, and it had been packed out. The Methodists got their name because of their methodical and disciplined way of life. Unlike the Church of England which was rather like a club for wealthy people dressed in their best, the Methodists attracted ordinary working people to their services. He had heard about their acts of charity to relieve suffering, and this appealed to Equiano.

That evening, the minister invited him to chapel. The place was overflowing with people. The preacher was in high spirits, throwing his arms around as if he was a madman. Several members of the congregation were on their feet, very emotional, and one or two seemed to be swooning. A bit different to what he had seen in the parish churches of London, where the buildings were half empty and the congregation looked half asleep! Here, in the Methodist chapel, guests were allowed to share their experiences of how God had saved them. Baskets full of buns and mugs of water were brought out and handed around. Equiano had read about such things in the Scriptures. Now he could see them for himself. How he loved it!

Chapter 15

Could the Methodists help him in his battle against the slave trade – where human suffering was all too evident? His main concern was with the appalling conditions on the slave ships. He had no objection as yet to slavery itself. After all, in certain societies, such as his own in Africa, he knew that slaves were fairly treated and happy.

So when his old friend Dr Irving from Pall Mall suggested they set up a plantation in Jamaica together, he agreed to become a partner in the project. Besides, he would treat his slaves with care and affection, just as they were treated in Africa.

And he would be able to make a little profit at the same time!

In November 1775 they sailed for the West Indies in the *Morning Star*. They bought slaves in Jamaica and then sailed south-west to what was called the Mosquito Coast (now Honduras) in Central America. Irving and Equiano carefully chose the place for the plantation in rich soil near the bank of a river. The climate was very hot and humid, and the crew seemed to spend most of their time batting at mosquitoes that kept whining around their ears. They cleared woodland and planted fruit and vegetables which they would exchange with the native Indians for oil and fish. There was so much to do that they even worked on Sundays.

They lived out in the open with just a roof over their heads – with the mosquitoes for company. And yet they lived in safety, nothing was lost or stolen. Equiano had no doubt that if they did this in Europe they would probably have their throats cut on the very first night.

What *did* frighten them at night were the roars of the wild beasts in the forest. So they made fires all around them to keep them away. As it turned out none of the animals ever hurt them, except snakes which bit two of the natives and one of the slaves. Dr Irving immediately gave them each half a tumbler of strong rum with plenty of Cayenne pepper in it. All three survived!

Soon after this a messenger brought them a richly engraved stick. It belonged to the governor and it signified his intention to pay them a visit – a business visit! He would be coming to collect tribute (gifts and taxes). The governor was a highly respected man who looked after the people well, listening to complaints and settling disputes. They were used to handing over the rum, sugar and gunpowder that he demanded.

But to Equiano's utter disbelief and horror, the governor arrived accompanied by a gang of thugs, whose wild shouts could be heard through the trees long before they were caught sight of. They were all out of their mind with drink. What on earth were they to do with them? They had no choice but to feed them and hope they would be on their way as soon as possible. But things got worse and the governor became very drunk and abusive. He got himself into an argument with one of the chiefs – a man called Captain Plasmyah who would never have hurt a fly – not even a whining mosquito.

Then the governor hit him and seized his lovely gold-laced hat. There was absolute uproar! Dr Irving tried to calm everyone down, but being by nature rather a feeble man no one took a blind bit of notice of him. Things soon got so bad that Irving decided to leave the house and go and hide in the woods, leaving Equiano to cope on his own. He would love to have tied the governor to a tree and had him flogged but thought better of it – after all, the governor's men outnumbered his own.

Suddenly an idea came to him. It was something that he had read about many years ago in his dear friend Richard Baker's *Life of Christopher Columbus*. When the explorer had visited Jamaica on his fourth voyage he had used his knowledge of an imminent lunar eclipse to frighten the inhabitants into giving his men food and drink. Could Equiano do something similar to restore order here in Honduras?

He beckoned to the governor and pointed up to the sky. 'Look. God lives there! He is angry with you! You are brothers and must not quarrel.' His voice resonated in the still air. He took out his Bible and held it up. Eyes began to turn towards him. 'If you don't stop quarrelling and go away quietly, I shall read from my Bible and tell God to strike you all dead!'

Absolute silence.

Equiano had not the faintest idea whether it would work or not. Would he be laughed at? Would the governor's men take him away and flog him? But much to his relief the commotion died down. Everyone went away peacefully. Dr Irving returned from the woods. And Captain Plasmyah even had his hat with the gold lacing returned!

The people were so grateful to Equiano for doing this (and to the doctor for treating their snake bites) that they put on a feast to celebrate. There were great delicacies to eat – tortoises, dried turtle and alligator which looked like fresh salmon but was too rich for Equiano to stomach. They quaffed back a drink called casade that was made from fermented roast pineapples but it looked just like pigswill!

Afterwards there was dancing, the men and women dancing separately, just as they did back home in Africa. One of the chiefs wore animal skins and feathers. On his head was a kind of grenadier's cap with prickles coming out of it like those of a porcupine. Every so often he would make a noise resembling the cry of an alligator. Terrified by the whole experience, the doctor decided to go over and dance with the women. But they quickly shooed him away and he had to return to the men.

The end of May brought the rainy season to Honduras. And it continued until August. Disaster! The rivers overflowed and their crops were washed away. Could this be God's punishment for them working on Sundays? Equiano thought so. He had had enough of the place and longed to return to Europe.

Even though he was a free Negro he faced many obstacles on his way back. The first night, just down river, a schooner approached. Its owner explained how they were short of hands and wanted Equiano to work for them as a sailor. He thanked him for the offer but said no. At this the owner went wild and started swearing, then got his crew to tie ropes around his ankles and wrists, and hoist him up. When Equiano pleaded for mercy the captain brought out a musket from his cabin and threatened to shoot him if he did not shut up. There he remained until early the next morning when the captain was distracted and he luckily managed to escape.

By the spring of 1777 Equiano had arrived safely back in Plymouth, Devon. He stayed a few days in Exeter before going to London. How wonderful it was to tread on English soil again. And what tales he had to tell. He had been a trader in the Caribbean, a wigmaker in London, a chemist in the Arctic and a slave owner on a Jamaican plantation. It was scarcely believable. Yet it was all true.

And what fresh opportunities would he have in the capital?

Chapter 16

London, 1779. Equiano was a free man, working as a servant for Matthias Macnamara, the former governor of Senegambia in West Africa. He was living at No.17 Hedge Lane, Charing Cross, in the West End of London. His life at sea lay behind him and he had no intention of returning to it. He had been cheated and abused once too often.

Many other servants worked in Macnamara's house, and Equiano got on well enough with all of them. But when he invited them to join him for evening prayers they just laughed at him. Macnamara, however, was more understanding. He took him seriously and brought him down to his study. He was evidently a busy man as papers were piled high on his desk but he still found time to listen to him. When Equiano had finished Macnamara made a suggestion. Why didn't he consider trying to convert people overseas by becoming a Christian missionary in Africa.

Equiano was unsure. He had only recently taken up his Bible and held no position in any Church.

Macnamara smiled and took up his quill from its stand. 'Don't worry. I'll see to it that you will be treated with respect. You will go as an ordained priest.'

And so he wrote a letter to the Bishop of London, recommending Equiano as a man with good morals and ideal for the purpose. If he had been accepted, this would have set Equiano's career on a different course. As it happened, the Bishop decided against sending out a new missionary to Africa. But as one door now closed, another was soon to open in Equiano's life.

When he was off duty he often spent an hour or

two in one of the fashionable coffee houses nearby, such as Anderton's or Peel's in Fleet Street or the Hungerford Coffee House in The Strand. Only men were allowed into the coffee houses with their richly panelled walls, fine works of art and fireplaces big enough to tether your horse in. Some treated them as their private clubs; others treated them as their offices. (How much better off was he to be a servant in the West End than in Wapping or Southwark, poorer areas where all he would have found was gin shops!)

Sitting in chairs carved from dark wood behind even darker long tables, they smoked pipes of tobacco and discussed business while the coffee boys rushed around pouring coffee, not into cups and mugs as today, but into dishes for them to drink. In these establishments men would also have the opportunity of reading books and the London newspapers, and dealing with their correspondence. The coffee house owners provided pens, ink and paper for their clientele, and Equiano began to use all these facilities. Sometimes he thought he got a few odd looks from the other customers but he did not let these bother him as he sat writing. In fact he began to inundate the editors of London newspapers such as the *Morning Post* and the *Daily Advertiser* with letters about topical subjects – war, commerce and, of course, the slave trade. To achieve maximum attention he would 'pick fights' with people and there would be a chain of correspondence, all signed 'Gustavus Vassa the African.'

One morning an article he read in one of these papers deeply shocked him. He made detailed notes on what he read and took them straight away to his friend, Granville Sharp - 'Greeny'. The article described the terrible sequence of events that had occurred a year or so before on a slave ship. The reason the article appeared only now was that the whole matter had at last reached the law courts.

Sharp studied Equiano's notebook. The slave ship *Zong*, under the command of Luke Collingwood, had sailed from Africa with about 470 African slaves on board, destination the West Indies.

Not far into their journey, over sixty of the slaves had died and many others were very sick. Collingwood realized that he had a serious problem on his hands. If the slaves continued to die from natural causes he would lose a lot of money.

So he decided to pretend that his ship was running out of drinking water, and to save the healthy slaves and the crew he would throw some of the sickest slaves overboard. This would make it possible for him to claim on the insurance. Actually, the ship had plenty of water at this point – 200 gallons – and the water butts were filling up every day in the heavy rain. But slaves continued to be thrown overboard – and 133 perished in the ocean.

Sharp looked towards the street windows. He seemed to mouth the words 'cold-blooded murderers.' He turned back to Equiano. His mind was made up. Collingwood and his officers had to pay for what they had done. They must be brought before the courts.

Although the insurers refused to pay out, no further action was taken against Luke Collingwood and his crew. Some people, such as the writer James Tobin, doubted that the *Zong* incident had ever happened – that the whole thing was just wicked lies and propaganda made up by those who wanted to abolish the slave trade. (Just as there are those today who deny the full extent of the Nazi Holocaust.) They argued that the slave ships provided the slaves with plenty of space and several meals a day, including the best African sauces! That they were given water to wash in after breakfast, that their accommodation was perfumed with frankincense and lime juice and that songs and dances were put on every evening before dinner.

★ ★ ★

What could Equiano do to contradict these lies and to expose to the public the true horror of what was going on? The kindest master he had ever had was the Quaker, Robert King. He knew that the Quakers as a group were greatly opposed to the barbarity practised by some slave owners. So, in

1785, he asked to give a speech to the Quakers at their meeting house in Lombard Street near St Paul's Cathedral in the City of London. His voice echoed around the stone building as he spoke in his strong, confident tone about the 'oppressed, needy and much degraded Negroes'. He showed he was determined to do everything he could to put an end to their traffic.

Equiano was now forty years old and his name was becoming well known in influential circles. So much so that next year a committee of gentlemen sent for him. The gentlemen were responsible for looking after the black poor in London. The number of blacks in London had been growing ever since 1783 when slaves had been promised their freedom in England for fighting on the King's side during the American War of Independence. The gentlemen told him about a scheme to take Africans to Sierra Leone. They would be expected to work hard when they got there but they would be free Negroes. Equiano was asked to superintend the expedition. He hesitated, as this would produce a

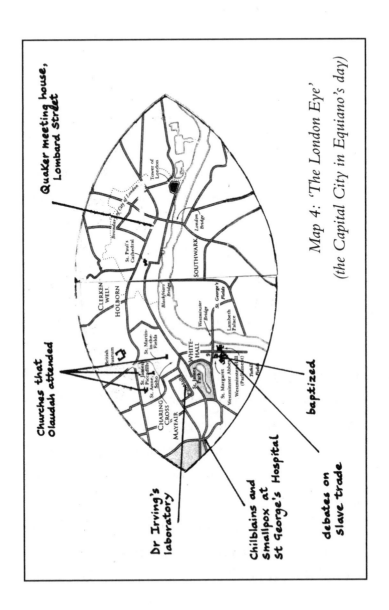

Quaker meeting house, Lombard Street

Churches that Olaudah attended

Dr Irving's laboratory

Chilblains and smallpox at St George's Hospital

debates on slave trade

baptized

Tower of London

Boundary of City of London

London Bridge

St Paul's Cathedral

SOUTHWARK

CLERKEN WELL

HOLBORN

Blackfriars Bridge

Westminster Bridge

St George's Fields

Lambeth Palace

British Museum

St Martin-in-the-Fields

WHITE HALL

St James Piccadilly

St Anne's Soho

St James's Park

St Margaret Westminster Abbey (Parliament)

Tothill Fields

CHARING CROSS to MAYFAIR

Map 4: 'The London Eye'
(the Capital City in Equiano's day)

head on clash with the slave dealers. The committee ignored his objections and put him in charge anyhow.

There were plenty of people around who thoroughly disapproved of the scheme. A writer called Gordon Turnbull argued that the black poor in London did not deserve charity, that they were living proof that Africans were lazy and had not the strength of character to find work.

It turned out that Equiano was not the best of appointments after all. He did not manage to get all the weapons and ammunition loaded on to the ships in time. But his task was not made easier by all the usual cheating. For example, the government paid for provisions which were never actually bought – the money going into agents' pockets. So there were no beds or clothing or medicines. Equiano felt duty-bound to report the corruption, and when he did so he was instantly dismissed.

So he turned to other methods of drawing attention to the terrible abuses. Knowing that King George III was hostile to abolishing the slave trade, he decided instead to try to persuade his wife, Queen Charlotte, to act. In 1788 he sent her a petition on behalf of millions of his African countrymen 'who groan under the lash of tyranny in the West Indies.' He begged her to put an end to the inhuman traffic of slavery and to raise the 'wretched Africans' from 'the condition of brutes' to become men with rights and dignity.

He knew only too well that his petition would be deeply unpopular with many powerful people in Britain who supported the slave trade. A common argument went that working conditions for Africans in the West Indies were more humane than in Africa, and that traders were doing the slaves a favour by taking them away from their homeland. What nonsense! Equiano would retort loudly in public at every opportunity. Other people with a vested interest in the slave trade argued that without it Britain would no longer be a wealthy country. Equiano replied to them that English workers would actually be richer as they would be able to supply their goods to the African market. In fact the only people who would suffer would be those who manufactured neck-yokes, collars, chains, hand-cuffs, leg-bolts, thumb screws, iron muzzles and other instruments of torture used in the slave trade.

But the problem still was that nearly every middle class family in Britain had some connection with the slave trade – the 'respectable trade.' Had Equiano completely lost his senses? Could he ever seriously expect to win sufficient support in England to ban such a profitable enterprise?

Chapter 17

Very few people had ever come into direct contact with the slave trade, so it is not surprising that there were only a handful of protesters. As these possible trouble-makers were scattered around the country, the British government considered them harmless.

All this began to change in 1787 when Granville Sharp formed the Society for Effecting the Abolition of the Slave Trade. Based in London, the Society had its own special seal depicting a chained and kneeling African. Arched over the figure to make a halo were the words 'Am I not a man and a brother?'

Local abolitionist groups soon sprouted across the country. The Baptist, Methodist and Quaker churches also spoke out strongly against the slave trade; and in Parliament, a number of MPs started to make speeches to raise public awareness. Equiano took a keen interest in these activities, and his name (Gustavus Vassa) appears on letters of protest written by the so-called 'Sons of Africa.'

He was not the only black African to take part in the campaign. Just a stone throw from where he had been staying with the Guerins in Westminster, lived Ignatius Sancho. Equiano had probably seen him – perhaps at church, perhaps in his grocer's shop. And if he had not seen him, he would certainly have read something that he had written. Using the pseudonym 'Africanus,' Sancho wrote letters and articles condemning the slave trade. But he died in 1780 before the campaign had really built up a head of steam.

Another black African campaigner, Quobna Ottobah Cugoano, went further and in 1787 published a book: *Thoughts and Sentiments on the Evil and Wicked Traffic of the Human Species.* In the book he gives an example of a slave who received twenty-four lashes of the whip because he went to church instead of going to work! Cugoano blamed all British people for allowing slavery to exist and encouraged slaves to rebel against their masters. But soon after writing these passionate words Cugoano mysteriously disappears from the scene.

In 1789 the French Revolution began. The Bastille prison was stormed. The revolutionaries echoed the sentiments of the American Declaration of Independence (1776), that men are created equally. There were calls for 'liberty, equality and fraternity'. And for the abolition of the French slave trade. It was no coincidence that Equiano chose the same year to publish his autobiography. He had been encouraged by his friends to write it and had been scribbling away at it over the previous few years. They also helped him check it over. By writing it, his aim was to draw attention to 'one of the greatest evils now existing on the earth' and 'to put a speedy end to a traffic both cruel and unjust.'

Equiano had been one of a handful of fortunate ones. Hundreds of thousands of others had not been so lucky. The publication of a book by a black African writer would also prove to the world that Africans were neither 'sub-human' nor illiterate, as many white people chose to believe.

The book's full title was *The Interesting Narrative of the Life of Olaudah Equiano, or Gustavus Vassa the African*. It was originally printed in two volumes and ran into 530 pages. In the introduction he describes himself as 'unlettered,' by which he meant he did not have a formal education, and his book as 'wholly devoid of literary merit,' by which he meant not very well written.

It was not the first time Equiano had got into print. Ever since being sacked from the Sierra Leone scheme, he had time on his hands to write articles for the London newspapers and was beginning to make a name for himself. There were already in print stories by slave ship surgeons and slave ship captains who had been converted to anti-slavers. The best known of these was the slaver turned clergyman, John Newton – a man shaped like one of the barrels on his old ships – who said of the trade 'I think I should have quitted it sooner had I considered it as I do now.' The fact that these arguments against the slave trade should now come from Olaudah Equiano, an African – a victim of the slave trade – made them rather special.

To print thousands of copies of any book costs a publisher a great deal of money, and there is no way of knowing if a new author will sell enough copies to justify the expense. No publisher was willing to risk backing Equiano. If he had wished, he could probably have got funding from the Quakers or the Society for Effecting the Abolition of the Slave Trade. Instead, he decided to go it alone and self-publish the book. He kept a list of the names of people ('subscribers') who paid for and ordered copies of the book in advance. Remembering only too well how white people had cheated him in the past, he realised that if sales went well, all of the profits this time would go to him rather than to a publisher – just as they had done with his glass tumblers back in St Eustatia!

In all there were 311 subscribers. They included members of the royal family such as the Prince of Wales and the Duke of York, MPs, the Lord Mayor of London and many churchmen, including the bishops of Bangor, Chester, London and Worcester. When it was published, the price of the book (unbound) was seven shillings (equivalent to about £28 today) and six shillings to subscribers (£24). Equiano offered a discount to anyone buying six copies or more. At first it was only for sale in a dozen London bookshops. Eventually it could be bought right across the land – anywhere from a grocer's in Birmingham to a bookshop in Sandwich, Kent; from Equiano's lodging in Edinburgh to a draper's shop in Belfast! Tens of thousands of Britons were introduced to the life of a slave who ended up earning his freedom.

Then, off he went on a book tour – the first book tour on record. He toured England, Scotland and Ireland, jolting and rattling along roads full of ruts and pot holes with a wagon load of books that in moments of crisis he would thumb through and talk to. In his pockets he carried letters of recommendation from important and well-respected people. Travel was slow in this period. Unlike today, the government took no interest in keeping the roads in good repair. Although some local businessmen, farmers and traders had sometimes improved short stretches by setting up turnpike trusts and charging tolls for vehicles to use them, journeys by road were difficult and uncomfortable at the best of times, and impossible altogether when the weather turned bad. But despite these obstacles Equiano never gave up, venturing as far as Ireland where he found the people most hospitable. He even dared to travel to Bristol where slavers with huge pot bellies and with fingers like sausages had their businesses. Not only did he travel there without a bodyguard, but he found some more subscribers too!

Equiano also distributed pamphlets against the use of American and West Indian sugar. After all, anyone in Britain using this sugar by spreading jam on their bread, or who ate cakes, was participating in the crime of slavery by consuming one of its key products, and Britain's biggest import. (Logically, the same arguments could have been used against anyone who smoked tobacco or who took snuff, or who drank rum or brandy.)

One poet of the period called a cup of tea a 'blood-sweetened beverage.' A pamphleteer pricked the conscience of tea-drinkers by getting them to consider, as they sweetened their tea, how one sugar lump may have cost the poor slave a groan, a second lump a bloody stroke with a whip. As a result of the leafleting, it is believed that somewhere between a third of a million and half a million people in Britain boycotted sugar. One of these was a six-year-old boy, Panton Plymley, who stopped polishing his shoes because he had been told that shoe polish contained sugar! Anyone who had such a sweet tooth that they simply could not live without sugar was advised to buy Indian sugar. That was produced by free men. This is much like someone today who buys 'fair trade' chocolate or coffee, knowing that those who have picked the beans have worked in humane conditions and have received reasonable pay.

Whenever he could, Equiano would seize the opportunity during these tours to speak against the slave trade as well as sell plenty of copies of his book. He could make his voice heard at the back of a crowded hall and spoke with confidence. Some of those who came out to listen found such anger in his voice that it frightened them.

On one of these tours he attended a meeting of the Lunar Society in Birmingham – so-called because they met on the Monday nearest each full moon and there was enough light for their members to see themselves home. There he rubbed shoulders with some of the most well known scientists and businessmen of the day, including Josiah Wedgwood, the pottery manufacturer. Wedgwood was to produce a special china medallion with the seal of the Society for Effecting the Abolition of the Slave Trade.

On another tour, this time of Cambridgeshire,

the Reverend Dr Peter Peckard, Vice Chancellor of Cambridge University, himself a keen abolitionist, introduced him to Susannah Cullen from Ely and they soon became good friends. Her father was a well-to-do small farmer and owned pasture land in several Cambridgeshire villages.

In almost no time at all Equiano had built up a whole network of friends across the country – from Shrewsbury in the west to Norwich in the east. They would put him up overnight and help him sell his book. Many were members of local branches of the Society for Effecting the Abolition of the Slave Trade or held positions of power and influence. For example, Samuel Neilson, the hot-headed draper in Belfast who sold his book, was also the editor of a radical newspaper called the *Northern Star* that covered the campaign against the slave trade with great enthusiasm.

The *Narrative* was a runaway success. Readers loved it – it was a travel book, full of descriptions of exotic places. It was a fascinating biography, full of lively detail. And, because of all the terrible hardship and suffering, it was a real 'tear-jerker'. The book quickly sold out, and by the end of 1789 he was publishing a second edition. In all, there were nine editions. By the time of this last edition he had managed to reduce its cost to only five shillings (£20 in today's money, about the cost of the average hardback) which enabled it to reach a larger readership still. The book was also published in North America and was translated into Dutch, German and Russian. It proved a best-seller and made him a lot of money. He no longer needed to work and instead began to live the life of a gentleman. He was able to lend money, and could even afford to lose money if the borrower did not pay up.

Many years before, he had started life as a thing, an object, to be bought by one master after another. Now he was well on his way to becoming an international celebrity!

Chapter 18

Public interest in the campaign to abolish the slave trade continued to gather momentum. This was helped partly by the red-haired campaigner Thomas Clarkson who, just like Equiano, made marathon tours on horseback around the country, attending meetings and making speeches. Clarkson made it his particular business to visit the docks in Liverpool which was one of the great centres of the slave trade. He decided that it would be safer to travel by night. But news of his visit still leaked out, and he had to fight off an assassination attempt by slave traders on the pier. When he eventually got on board the ships he was shocked by what he saw. No amount of words would describe the suffering. What he really wanted was a more visual form to awaken the public conscience. Cameras and photographs had not yet been invented so he had to draw what he saw. He drew a plan of the interior of a Liverpool slave ship called *Brookes* that showed slaves packed spoon wise, head to toe and toe to head. Every space was filled. The slaves had no room in which to turn. It was produced as a poster and plastered around the country, horrifying those who saw it. In 1788 the government passed an Act of Parliament that reduced the number of slaves that a slave ship was allowed to carry, but even then conditions on board were still appalling.

Equiano and Thomas Clarkson were watching from the gallery when, on 18th April 1791, a debate on the slave trade opened in the House of Commons in London. Clarkson was not optimistic. He had counted up in advance the way he expected MPs to vote and told Equiano that they would lose.

The debate opened and a puny figure rose to

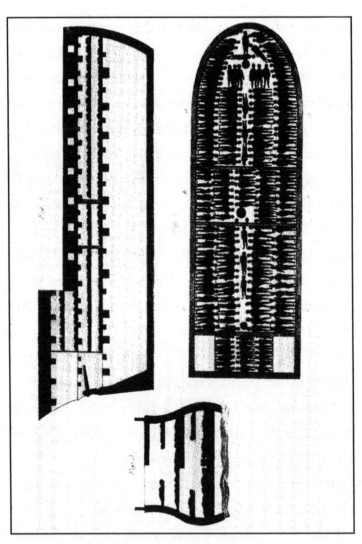

The slave ship Brookes

speak. This was William Wilberforce or 'the shrimp' as he was nicknamed.

'It has been claimed that an end to the trade will be a disaster for our economy. But this is not so. Far from hurting our traders it will help them. Africa will trade directly with us.'

A very tall man, wearing a dazzling green dragoon's uniform, jumped to his feet. His name was Banastre Tarleton, MP for Liverpool, and his two brothers were in the slavery business. His tone was defiant. 'What is this craze for abolition? Do the Africans object to the trade?' He shook his fist. 'Have they asked that it be ended? I think not.'

Clarkson felt the temperature of his blood rising by a degree or two.

No sooner than Tarleton had sat down than another pro-slaver, even taller than Tarleton, joined him. Were all those in favour of the trade giants, and were all the abolitionists pygmies?

'If it is true that the slaves are miserable they would not wear all the ornaments that they do around their necks. What further proof is needed that they must be happy?'

Equiano simply could not believe what he was hearing. Had his opponents convinced themselves that these things were true just to satisfy their consciences?.

The abolitionists' case was not helped by disturbances on the island of St Dominique where a slave revolt had broken out two months earlier and was gaining a hold. This was a disaster for the anti-slavery movement. The planters blamed the abolitionists for stirring up the slaves to fight for their rights.

After two days the House voted 163 to 88 against abolishing the slave trade. Clarkson had been horribly right in his calculations. Slave ports breathed a huge sigh of relief. Bloated merchants celebrated with huge roast beef dinners. In Liverpool the church bells rang and in Bristol a cannon was fired, there was a firework display and a half-day's holiday.

But abolition petitions continued to flood into Parliament from all over the country. In all there were 519 of them. One petition from Edinburgh was so long that, when unrolled, it stretched the whole length of the House of Commons floor. Another from Manchester contained twenty thousand signatures, which was nearly two thirds of the adult male population. Petitions from some small towns carried the signature of everyone able to write.

On the evening of 2nd April 1792, a new debate about the slave trade began in Parliament. A chandelier cast a dim glow over the tiers of benches where MPs sat in their gowns and powdered wigs. The narrow galleries for the visitors were filled right up. One of those visitors was Equiano.

The Speaker, in his long flowing wig and three-cornered hat, opened the debate. William Wilberforce was again the first to speak, and he spoke out against the horrors of the 'middle passage.' There were roars of approval from the MPs on his side of the House as the little man sat down again.

But it was soon the turn of the giants. Banastre Tarleton, M.P. for Liverpool was soon on his feet.

'Those who have signed the petitions do not know what they are talking about. I can assure my fellow MPs that the death rate on slave ships is negligible, just four and a half percent. And as for the signatures on those petitions, many people have been forced to sign, including the sick and passers-by. Others have been bribed into signing with offers of gifts.'

The debate went on all night. Candles flickered from their brackets along the side pillars. The MPs yawned openly during the longer speeches, hissed and booed at those they despised, stamped their buckled shoes and tapped their walking canes when they agreed. It ended with a grand speech against the slave trade from the Prime Minister, William Pitt, who summed up by admitting that 'there is no nation in Europe that has plunged so deeply into this guilt as Great Britain.'

As he finished his speech, shafts of light were beginning to pour in through the three large windows above the Speaker's chair; dawn was breaking. The MPs went off to cast their votes. The result was 230 to 85 in favour of *gradually* abolishing the slave trade over the next four years. Equiano was delighted, full of hope.

But before any bill could become a law it had to have the approval of the House of Lords. The problem was that the House of Lords was not prepared to see any abolition at all – not even a gradual one. One of those who sat in this House was the Archbishop of Canterbury, John Moore. He was most definitely in favour of continuing the trade for his wife's father was a planter from Carolina!

Events in France only made matters worse for the abolitionists. The revolutionaries had executed the King, Louis XVI, and were calling for war against all kings. As a result, hysteria swept across Britain. The government forbade political meetings of more than fifty people, and considered any abolitionist a possible revolutionary. The stream of antislavery books, newspaper articles and pamphlets quickly dried up and the anti-slave trade movement ground to a halt.

What more could Equiano do?

Chapter 19

Just four days after his all-night session in the House of Commons, Equiano married his friend Susannah Cullen. Effigies of a priest, a musician and a monk looked down at them from the dark beamed ceiling of St Andrew's Church in Soham, Cambridgeshire, as Equiano and Susannah sat in the medieval pews.

At this time, all weddings took place in church but there were no white wedding dresses. The bride simply wore her best clothes. For her wedding day Susannah had put on a long salmon-coloured dress with a hemline that almost reached the ground and a fine lace-edged scarf. Her pretty curled blond hair showed beneath a straw hat trimmed with ribbons. In her hand she clutched a small bouquet of flowers. Equiano looked every bit the English gentleman in his powdered white wig with side curls and crimson jacket worn over a high buttoned waistcoat, all set off with a white neckerchief and thick white stockings.

The marriage register reads:

'No.220 Gustavus Vassa (an African) of the Parish of St Martin in the Fields in the Co. of Middlesex, Bachelor, and Susannah Cullen of this Parish, Spinster, were married in this Church by Licence from Doctors Commons this seventh day of April in the Year One Thousand seven Hundred and ninety two...' Then appear the name of the curate, Charles Hill, and the signatures of the groom and bride.

They emerged from the church as man and wife. Susannah rested her hand on her husband's white gloved arm as they walked down the path with well-wishers cheering them on their way. The well-wisher making the most noise was Susannah's somewhat wayward sister, Mary. She was always

152

getting into scrapes with the people of Soham and was eventually to be transported to Australia for shoplifting.

Equiano was forty-seven years old. Susannah was thirty. A black man marrying a white English woman was just not done. For many people 'mixed' marriages were totally unacceptable. One outraged correspondent wrote to the *London Chronicle* newspaper in strongly racist terms, begging the public to 'save the natural beauty of Britons' from contamination. For him, Equiano was some kind of alien. No doubt there were others who found a mixed marriage repulsive. Perhaps they had gone along with his arguments against the barbarities of the slave trade, but marrying a white woman? Now he had gone too far. It was too much of a break with convention for them to stomach.

But Equiano was unconventional. He had no objection to mixed marriages and was in favour of getting rid of rules that made them difficult. It had appalled him years before in St Kitt's that a black woman had not been allowed to marry a white man in church and had ended up being married out at sea. But Equiano had defied the odds and had married a white woman. Now he could cross out the passage in his autobiography that said he was interested in meeting available young women!

So well known was Equiano that his wedding was even recorded in the London newspapers. The *General Evening Post* reported:

'Gustavus Vassa (Olaudah Equiano), the African, well known in England as the champion and advocate for procuring a suppression of the Slave Trade, was married at Soham, in Cambridgeshire to Miss Cullen, daughter of Mr Cullen of Ely, in the same County, in the presence of a vast number of people assembled on the occasion.'

Even his wedding had to be fitted in around book promotion. After spending ten days with his new wife he had planned to speed off to Scotland without her, so as to sell the fifth edition of his book. When it was time to leave, he had not the heart to tell her, and Susannah accompanied him to Paisley and Glasgow.

The couple were now very much in the limelight and there were plenty of journalists around then, as today, who took a keen interest in the private affairs as well as the public life of celebrities. On 30th May another newspaper, the *Gazeteer and New Daily Advertiser,* recorded that 'GUSTAVUS VASSA with his *white* wife, is at Edinburgh...' Why the emphasis on *white*?

Would the readers have been shocked?

If they were, that was as nothing compared with the shock that awaited Equiano next.

Chapter 20

Edinburgh, June 1792

Equiano was so astonished by what he read that he almost fell off his chair. But it was there in black and white in the newspaper. Santa Cruz! According to the *Oracle*, dated 25th April, sent to his Edinburgh lodgings by his friends in London, he had been born in the Danish island of Santa Cruz in the West Indies! What nonsense! He had never set foot on Santa Cruz in his whole life! What rascal had written these words? He read them again:

'Gustavus Vassa, who has publicly asserted that he

was kidnapped in Africa, never was upon that Continent, but was born and bred up in the Danish Island of Santa Cruz, in the West Indies.'

It was not the first time that there had been a question mark over his place of birth. His baptism and naval records say that he was born in Carolina. This time the accusation was being made in a letter from a pro-slaver. Was he trying to sabotage sales of Equiano's book?

As they continued on their tour of Scotland, Equiano was worried that he would be considered a fraud and that people would stop buying his *Narrative*. And that all his careful networking would come to nothing. Equiano had to hit back immediately. He wrote letters denying the charge and swore that he had been born in Africa.

When they returned from Scotland they set up home at Soham. Susannah mostly stayed there in the company of her parents while her husband roved around the country promoting his book. He may well have been away when their eldest daughter, Ann Mary (known as Maria) was born on

16th October 1793. What did the inhabitants of Soham make of a half-caste baby?

A second daughter, Joanna, was born on 11th April 1795. But any chance of a happy family life was soon to be ruined. Giving birth was dangerous at that time. Nothing was yet known about the risk of infection, and an untrained midwife living in the countryside would have delivered babies without washing her hands or sterilising the forceps. While managing to survive the delivery, it was easy for the mother to be infected with sepsis or puerperal fever.

We have no record of whether Susannah caught either of these. What we do know is that soon after giving birth to Joanna, Susannah became ill, and by December she had become so ill that she was advised to make her will. She did not survive the winter. On 16th February 1796 she died. She was just 34 years old.

Chapter 21

Equiano read from his Bible and asked it what he should do. When the winter turned to spring he left the two young girls in the company of their grandmother and went back to London. He lived first in Addle Street in the City, then in John Street, Tottenham Court Road. Finally he moved to Paddington Street. After a whole life time spent on the move, this would be his final abode. As Vincent Carretta says in his book *Equiano: The African*, 'Bordered on both sides by cemeteries, Paddington Street was a grimly appropriate place to end one's life.'

Equiano tried to pick up from where he had left off, but the death of his wife had a traumatic effect. Although his two daughters meant a great deal to him, Susannah had been his soul mate. Without her, he lost the will to live and started neglecting himself.

Just over a year later, on 31st March 1797, with his nurse Mrs Edwards by his bedside, Equiano died. He was 52 years old. His friend, Granville Sharp, visited him on his deathbed. He had completely lost his voice and could only whisper.

When he died, Equiano was almost certainly the wealthiest man of African descent living in England. He left a will whereas most people in Britain at this time did not own nearly enough to do this. He had household goods, clothes and his books which he kept in a chest. But most of his wealth came from selling his autobiography.

As for the couple's two daughters, Ann Mary died just four months after her father. An inscription on the outside wall of St Andrew's Church, Chesterton, Cambridge, reads:

Near this Place lies Interred
ANNA MARIA VASSA
Daughter of Gustavus Vassa the African
She died July 21 1797

Should simple village rhymes attract thine eye,
Stranger, as thoughtfully thou pasest by,
Know that there lies beside this humble stone
A child of colour haply not thine own.
Her father born of Afric's sun-burnt race,
Torn from his native fields, ah foul disgrace;
Through various toils, at length to Britain came
Espouse'd, so Heaven ordain'd, an English dame,
And follow'd Christ; their hope two infants dear.
But one, a hapless Orphan, slumbers here…

The younger daughter, Joanna Vassa, married
Henry Bromley, a minister, and lived to the ripe old
age of sixty-one. There is no record of them having
any children.

★ ★ ★

In 1807, ten years after Equiano's death, and twenty years after the campaign had begun, a bill abolishing the British slave trade passed both Houses of Parliament, and on 25th March King George III added his signature to it. After 1st May 1807 no slave ship was allowed to leave a British port. A commemorative medal was struck. It showed Britannia and bore the words 'I have heard their cry.'

But slavery still existed, and there were still over half a million black slaves on British plantations in the West Indies, working in the sugar-cane fields, sugar mills and boiling houses. All were destined to die at a young age. A quarter of a century passed until eventually, in 1833, slavery itself was abolished in the British colonies, plantation owners were compensated and the slaves were freed.

Men such as William Wilberforce and Parliament have usually been given all the credit for bringing the slave trade to an end, and ultimately slavery itself. It is undeniable that they played an important part. But sometimes history books are written as if freedom came as a gift from the whites – or from Britannia – to grateful slaves. What is often forgotten is that black people themselves were fighting to be freed – men such as Sancho and Cuguano, but above all Olaudah Equiano.

Through his book and in his articles, letters and speeches, he defended millions of people taken away by force from Africa and brought to America as slaves. In the early years of the campaign to abolish the slave trade, until his death in 1797, Equiano was their fiercest champion. Although he was not the only former slave to campaign against the slave trade, he was the main black speaker on behalf of the abolitionists. To the end of his life he remained true to his birth name, 'Olaudah' – the one with the loud voice.

Key dates in the life of Equiano

1745   According to Equiano, he was born in Benin, in modern-day Nigeria

1756   Captured by two men and a woman

1757   Arrived in London

1758   Expedition against Louisbourg during Seven Years War (1756-63)

1759   Baptized at St Margaret's Church, Westminster.

1763-66   Captive in West Indies

1766   Bought his freedom.

1767–68	London
1771	Voyage to West Indies
1773	Voyage to the North Pole
1775	Helps set up a plantation in Africa
1777–86	England
1785	Anti-slavery speech before Quakers in London
1786	Sierra Leone scheme
1787	Dismissed from Sierra Leone
1788	Presented Queen Charlotte with a petition against African slavery
1789	Published 1st edition of *The Interesting Narrative*

1792	*Oracle* newspaper claims Equiano was born in Santa Cruz, West Indies
	Debate on slave trade in House of Commons
1792	Married Susannah Cullen from Soham, Cambridgeshire
1796	Susannah died
1797	Equiano died in London

Where to find out more about Equiano

Useful books

The Interesting Narrative of the Life of Olaudah Equiano or Gustavus Vassa, the African by himself (Penguin 2nd edition, 2003)

An African's Life. The Life and Times of Olaudah Equiano, 1745-1797 by James Walvin (Continuum, 1998)

Equiano The African. Biography of a Self-Made Man by Vincent Carretta (University of Georgia Press, 2005)

Bury the Chains. The British Struggle to Abolish Slavery by Adam Hochschild (Macmillan, 2005)

Useful websites

www.bbc.co.uk/history/historic_figures/
equiano_olaudah.shtml

www.brycchancarey.com/equiano/

www.spartacus.schoolnet.co.uk/Sequiano.htm

www.understandingslavery.com

Acknowledgements

I would like to thank Evie Bunte, Lucy Harris, Oliver St john-jeffrey and Diana Williams for their helpful comments on earlier drafts of this book.